THE ILLUSTRATED NATURAL HISTORY

Scientific Consultants to the Series:

Masset Inlet on the Queen Charlotte Islands at dusk.

OF CANADA The Pacific Coast FRED BODSWORTH

Earth Science Consultant WALTER TOVELL, Curator, Department of Geology, Royal Ontario Museum. *Life Science Consultant* J. MURRAY SPEIRS, Department of Zoology, University of Toronto

Library of Congress Catalog Card Number: 73-105930

N.S.L. Natural Science of Canada Limited
58 Northline Road, Toronto 16, Ontario, Canada

Publisher: Jack McClelland
Editor-in-Chief: Peter Crabtree
Senior Editor: Michael Worek
Art Director: Peter Moulding
Visual Editor: Bill Brooks

Editorial Consultant: Pierre Berton

THE PACIFIC COAST

Art Director: Peter Moulding
Artists: Vlasta van Kampen/
Gordon McLean/Huntley Brown
Jerry Kozoriz/Harry Aalto

The richness of the sea

Contents

Prologue

THE LAND APART

The author — an international naturalist at work on the coast.

In the broad and infinitely varied tapestry of regions that make up the North American continent, the Pacific coast stands out as a land of giants. The continent's highest mountains rise abruptly from the sea, and the world's tallest trees, the largest as high as a 30-story building, scratch the clouds with their needly tips.

The greatest weight of living matter per acre in the world is found in areas such as Vancouver Island's Cathedral Grove, where virgin stands of the coastal rain forest's tremendous Douglas firs, cedars, hemlocks and Sitka spruce have survived the lumberman's saw. North America's highest peaks are also found in this Coast Mountain System and its Alaskan extension, not in the more celebrated Rockies farther inland. Mount McKinley, at 20,300 feet the continent's highest, is found in the Alaska Range; Mount Logan, 19,850 feet, Canada's highest, is in the St. Elias Mountains of southwestern Yukon.

But as a key to understanding the area's natural history, there is a more significant and revealing element of hugeness in the dimensions of its coastline. As a Canada goose migrating to its Alaskan nesting grounds might fly it, the B.C. coast from the U.S. border north to the Alaskan Panhandle is about 550 miles. Yet the actual coastline in that chaotic maze of twisting fiords and myriad islands is estimated to be more than 16,000 miles–a coastline five times as long as Canada is wide. In other words, there are about 30 miles of contorted shoreline for every straight-line mile reaching toward Alaska. These incredibly disparate figures point up more eloquently than anything else the basic nature of the mountainous coastal region.

The Pacific coast is not just a land beside the sea, it is a land literally *of* the sea, entwined and cradled by innumerable salt-water straits and fiords; the marine influence is stamped boldly on almost every feature. Its dramatic scenery of fiords and headlands, which can be seen on the popular cruise route of the Inside Passage to Alaska, was carved by the sea when rising sealevels flooded the great glacier-cut valleys left by the Pleistocene Ice Age. Its mild, humid climate, the principal natural factor determining its flora and fauna, and the creator of the towering rain forest that is the land's most famous trademark, is also a product of the sea. The clock that governs much of its day to day rhythm of life is the ebb and flow of ocean tides. The bulk of coastal life lives on, in, over, or by the ocean, and its major animal food chains, the savage eat-and-be-eaten exchange of proteins between prey and predator, have their origins in the rich, plankton pastures of the sea. And the commonest bird, even in downtown city areas, is the glaucous-winged gull.

Despite the fact that it is physically joined to a massive continent, this coastal region stands alone, like an island, with its own distinctive natural history and a scenic grandeur that neighbouring regions do not share. An area such as this with its own characteristic plant and animal life is known as a *biome* or *biotic region,* and as biotic regions go, this is one of the continent's smallest. It is, however, sharply differentiated, a land apart, a land with only weak ties to the continent of which it is part, but deep and pervading ties with the restless, embracing sea.

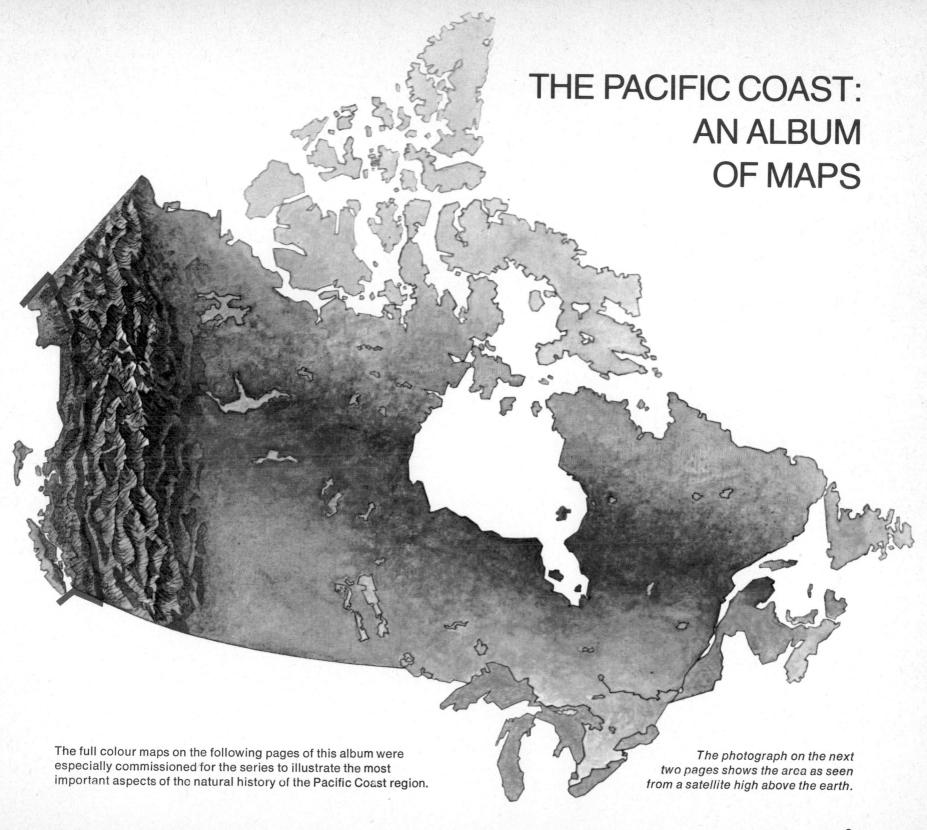

THE PACIFIC COAST: AN ALBUM OF MAPS

The full colour maps on the following pages of this album were especially commissioned for the series to illustrate the most important aspects of the natural history of the Pacific Coast region.

The photograph on the next two pages shows the area as seen from a satellite high above the earth.

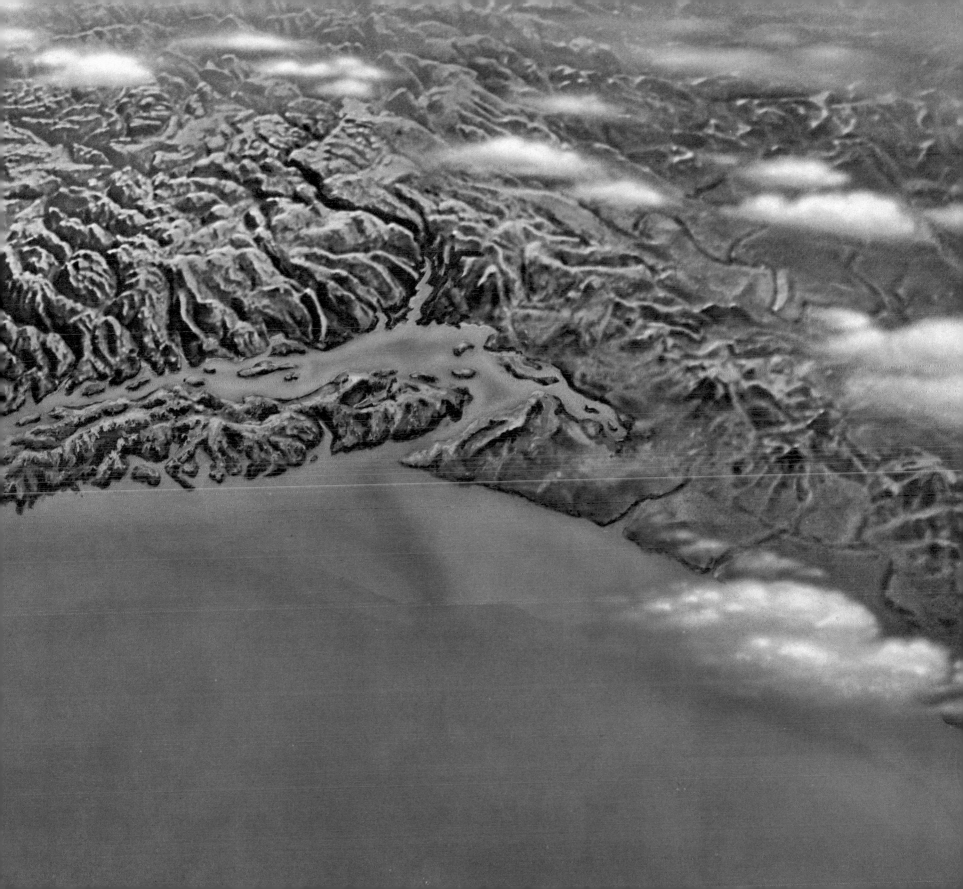

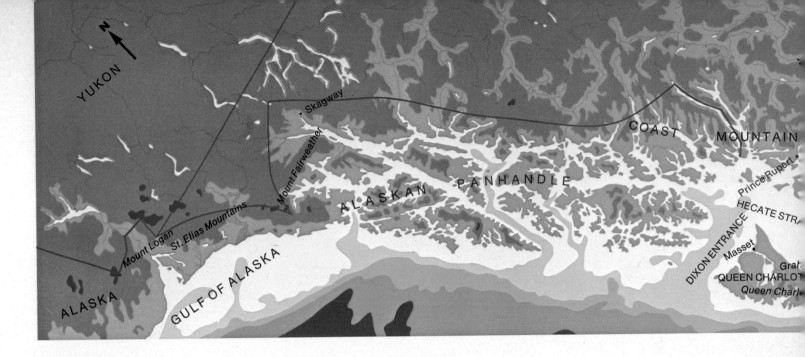

Places in the text

The map above shows the major places mentioned in the text. Each of the smaller maps below shows one aspect of the natural history of the region in greater detail.

Coastal landforms

Coastal System	Interior System
▬ ▬ ▬ Coastal Trough	

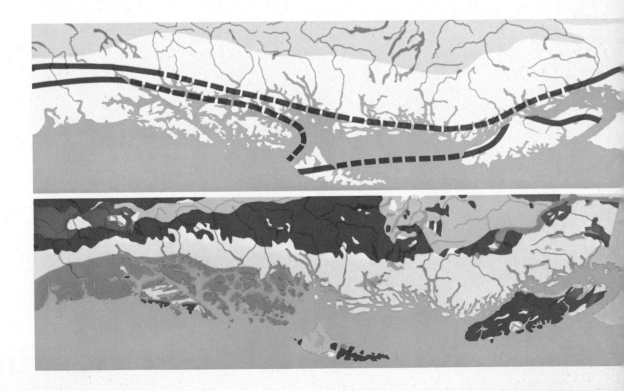

Geologic zones

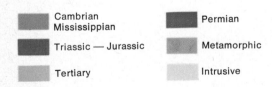

Cambrian Mississippian	Permian
Triassic — Jurassic	Metamorphic
Tertiary	Intrusive

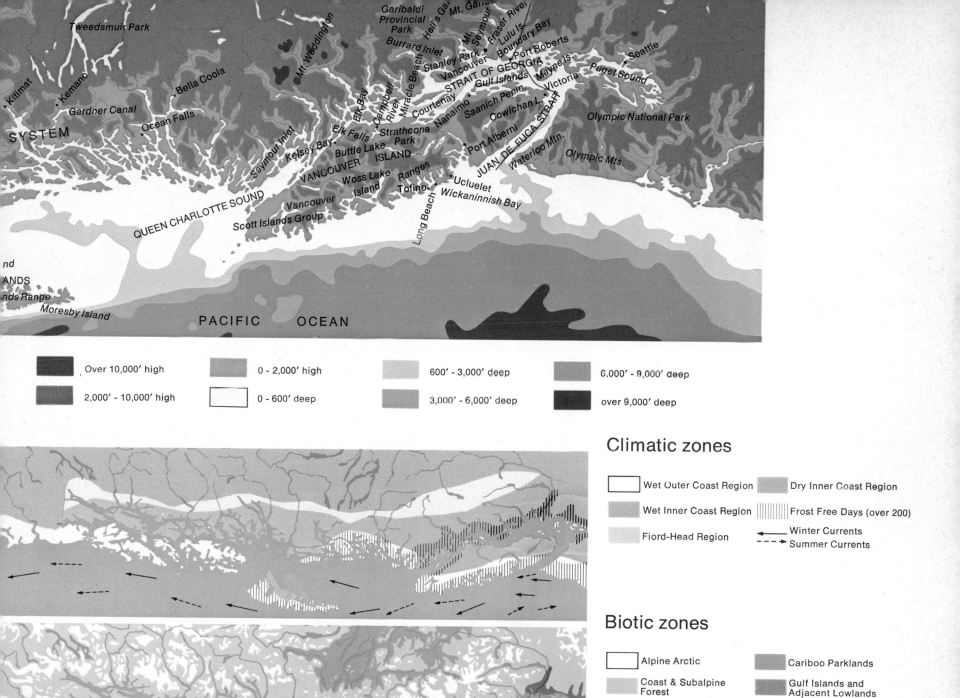

Tweedsmuir Park

Kitimat
Kemano
Gardner Canal
Bella Coola
Ocean Falls
SYSTEM
Seymour Inlet
Kelsey Bay
Elk Bay
Elk Falls
Buttle Lake
Woss Lake
Island
Mt. Waddington
Campbell River
Miracle Beach
Strathcona Park
VANCOUVER ISLAND
Vancouver Island
Scott Islands Group
QUEEN CHARLOTTE SOUND
Rangos
Tofino
Long Beach
Ucluelet
Wickaninnish Bay
Garibaldi Provincial Park
Burrard Inlet
Hell's Ga
Mt. Gari
Mt. Seymour
Stanley Park
Vancouver
Courtenay
Nanaimo
Fraser River
Lulu Is.
Boundary Bay
Port Roberts
STRAIT OF GEORGIA
Gulf Islands
Saanich Penin.
Cowichan L.
Mayne Is.
Victoria
Port Alberni
JUAN DE FUCA STRAIT
Waterloo Mtn.
Puget Sound
Seattle
Olympic National Park
Olympic Mts.

nd
ANDS
nds Range
Moresby Island

PACIFIC   OCEAN

▪ Over 10,000' high		▪ 0 - 2,000' high		600' - 3,000' deep	6,000' - 9,000' deep
2,000' - 10,000' high		0 - 600' deep		3,000' - 6,000' deep	over 9,000' deep

Climatic zones

▢ Wet Outer Coast Region	Dry Inner Coast Region
Wet Inner Coast Region	‖‖‖ Frost Free Days (over 200)
Fiord-Head Region	⟶ Winter Currents
	⇢ Summer Currents

Biotic zones

▢ Alpine Arctic	Cariboo Parklands
Coast & Subalpine Forest	Gulf Islands and Adjacent Lowlands

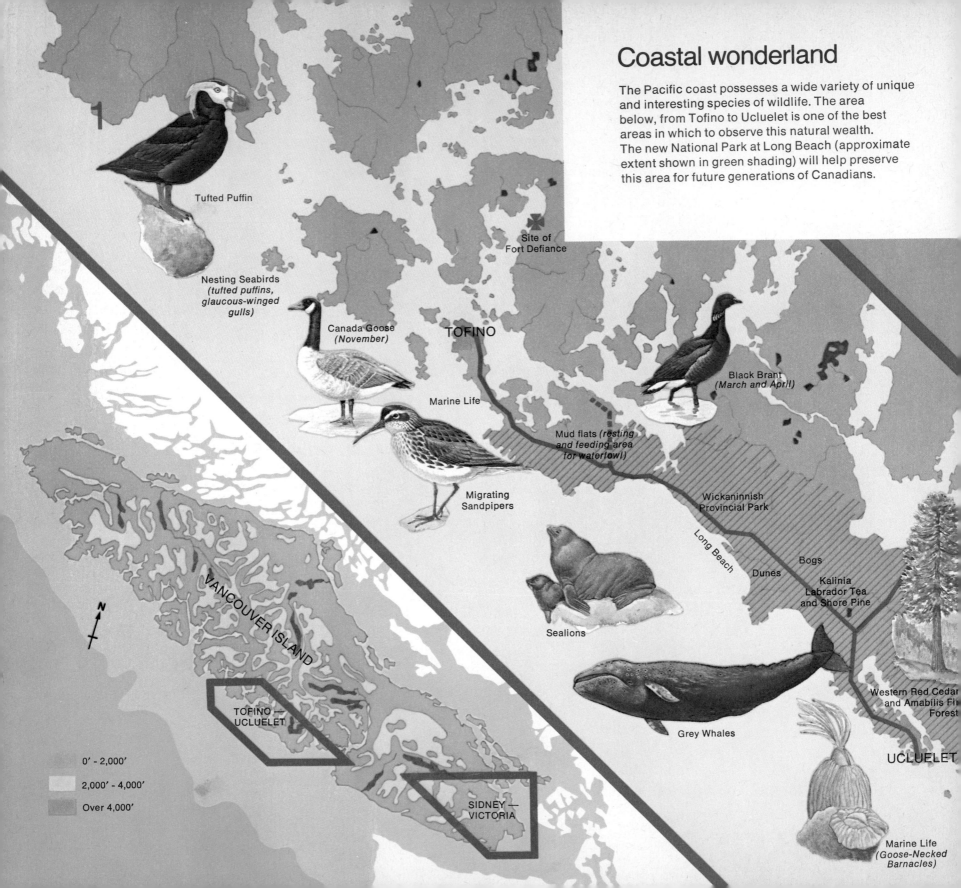

Coastal wonderland

The Pacific coast possesses a wide variety of unique and interesting species of wildlife. The area below, from Tofino to Ucluelet is one of the best areas in which to observe this natural wealth. The new National Park at Long Beach (approximate extent shown in green shading) will help preserve this area for future generations of Canadians.

Tufted Puffin

Nesting Seabirds
(tufted puffins, glaucous-winged gulls)

Site of Fort Defiance

Canada Goose
(November)

TOFINO

Marine Life

Black Brant
(March and April)

Mud flats *(resting and feeding area for waterfowl)*

Migrating Sandpipers

Wickaninnish Provincial Park

Long Beach

Dunes

Bogs

Kalinia Labrador Tea and Shore Pine

Sealions

VANCOUVER ISLAND

Grey Whales

Western Red Cedar and Amabilis Fir Forest

UCLUELET

TOFINO — UCLUELET

SIDNEY — VICTORIA

Marine Life
(Goose-Necked Barnacles)

0' - 2,000'

2,000' - 4,000'

Over 4,000'

N

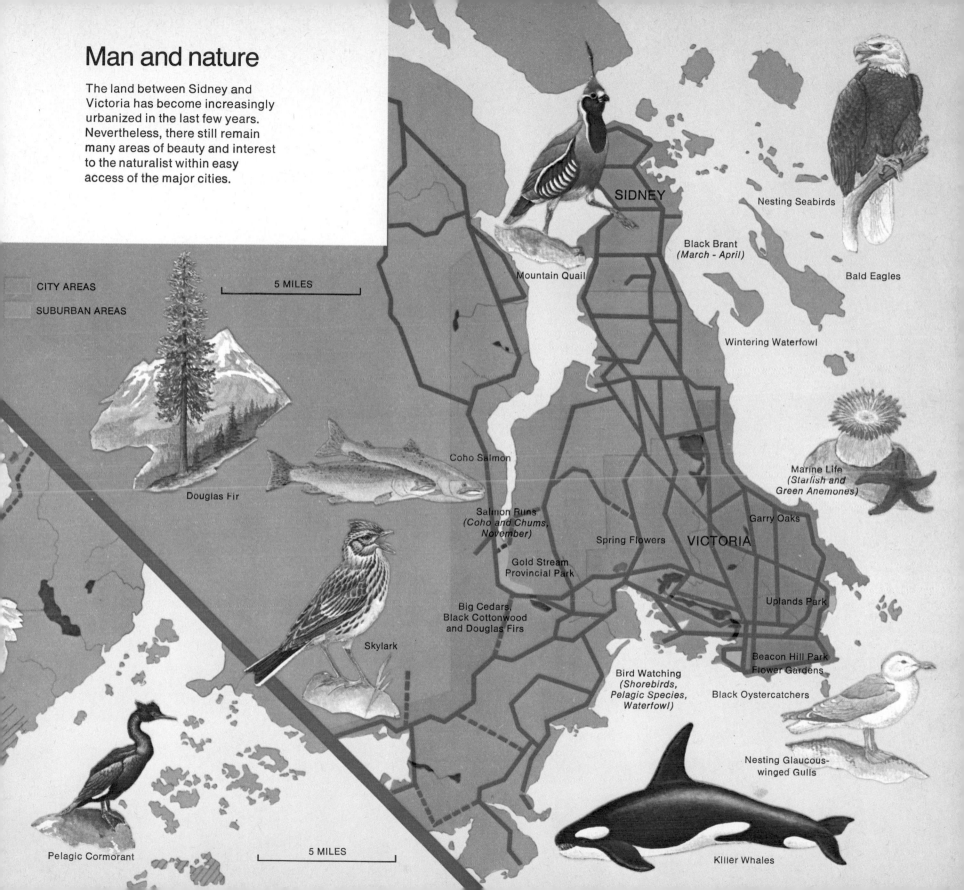

Man and nature

The land between Sidney and Victoria has become increasingly urbanized in the last few years. Nevertheless, there still remain many areas of beauty and interest to the naturalist within easy access of the major cities.

CITY AREAS

SUBURBAN AREAS

5 MILES

SIDNEY

Nesting Seabirds

Black Brant
(March - April)

Bald Eagles

Mountain Quail

Wintering Waterfowl

Douglas Fir

Coho Salmon

Marine Life
(Starfish and
Green Anemones)

Salmon Runs
(Coho and Chums,
November)

Spring Flowers

VICTORIA

Garry Oaks

Gold Stream
Provincial Park

Uplands Park

Big Cedars,
Black Cottonwood
and Douglas Firs

Skylark

Beacon Hill Park
Flower Gardens

Bird Watching
(Shorebirds,
Pelagic Species,
Waterfowl)

Black Oystercatchers

Nesting Glaucous-
winged Gulls

Pelagic Cormorant

5 MILES

Killer Whales

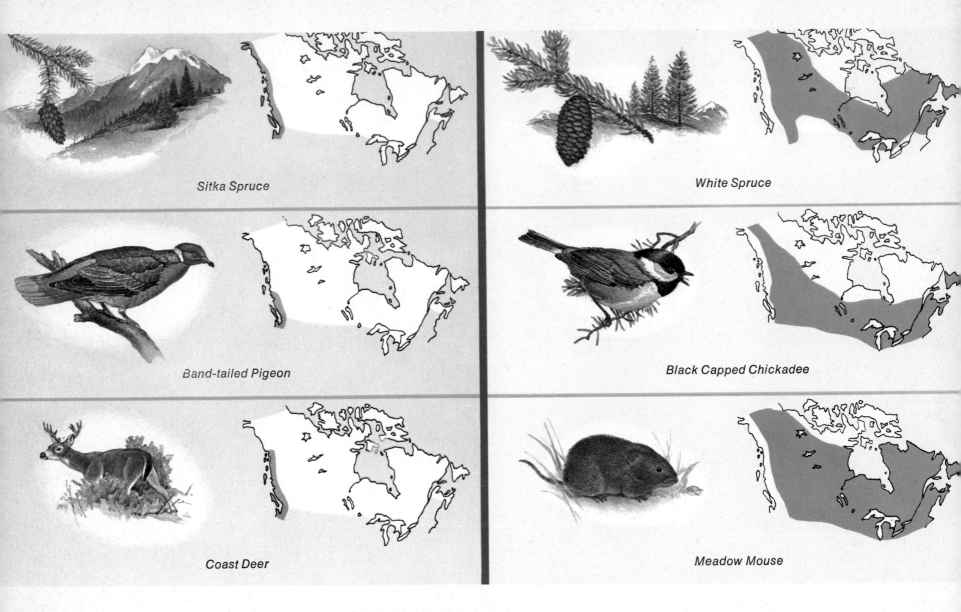

Sitka Spruce

White Spruce

Band-tailed Pigeon

Black Capped Chickadee

Coast Deer

Meadow Mouse

The cage we cannot see

The narrow strip of land bordering the Pacific is walled off by mountains and possesses a climate and living conditions very different from the rest of the continent. Many plants, trees and animals have become so adapted to these specialized habitat conditions that they can live nowhere else. This, in effect, makes the region an invisible cage. The orange portions of the maps show ranges of three species confined to the coast, and three others which have been unable to cross the mountain barrier.

PART ONE / THE REGION

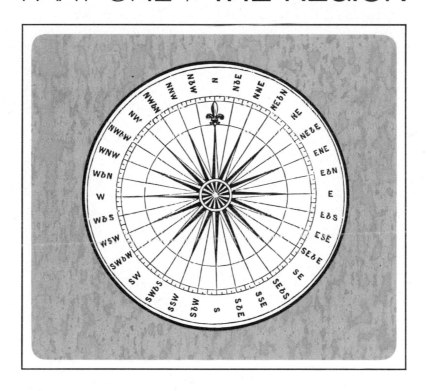

1 THE INVISIBLE CAGE

British Columbia has three major segments–on the eastern border, the Rocky Mountains; in the interior, a broad high plateau cut by river valleys and broken here and there by smaller mountain ranges; and on the west, rising out of the Pacific, a labyrinth of islands and the towering wall of the Coast Mountains. The ribbon of mountainous terrain along the Pacific that the geologists know as the Coastal System is the area covered by this book.

The Coastal Region has three main geological features. On the west are the offshore islands, the major ones being Vancouver Island which sits like a fat, 280-mile-long cigar off B.C.'s southern coast, and farther north the remote and isolated Queen Charlottes. Their backbone is formed by the Insular Mountains which run through Vancouver Island, dip under the sea for 180 miles before reappearing as the Queen Charlotte Ranges, then continue northward 400 miles as modest peaks of the outermost Alaskan Panhandle islands before finally rearing up as the soaring massif of the St. Elias Mountains along the curve of the Gulf of Alaska.

Between the islands and the mainland there is a long, trench-like depression known as the Coastal Trough. It starts in the south as the Gulf of California, rises above sealevel through California, Oregon and Washington, becomes submerged again in Puget Sound, and from there continues north along the Canadian coast as the Strait of Georgia, Queen Charlotte Sound and Hecate Strait.

The third and dominant feature of the area is the Coast Mountains of the mainland, an interlocking jumble of many ranges, with its braided network of fiords, and the spatter of islands formed by the tops of submerged mountains along the continent's rim.

Actually, our region doesn't include all of this Coastal System, for we are concerned with life zones, not geological ones, and in terms of the life they support the drier, rain-shadowed eastern slopes of the Coast Mountains are very different from the moist, ocean-facing, western slopes. The eastern slopes, though belonging geologically to the Coastal System, have climates, forests and fauna that link them biotically with the interior, so our natural history survey will extend to the summits of the Coast Mountains, a region only 50 to 150 miles wide, and not to the inland slopes beyond.

Despite its small size, this area harbours a plant and animal population very different from the rest of Canada. Its marine life is distinctive in that the Atlantic coast, 3,000 miles away, is the only other temperate region of Canada where similar life can occur; but there is further distinction even here, because the marine life of the Pacific coast is much more varied and abundant than that of the Atlantic. Its land life too shows a sharp "apartness."

Walled off by mountains and individualized by a climate strikingly different from that of adjoining regions, the west coast, with its mild, maritime climate, heavy rainfall and long, frost-free growing season, stands apart and forms a habitat unit matched nowhere else in North America. As a result the area has evolved a large number of distinctive species. Such species, characteristic of a region and not found outside it, are known as *endemics*. But no living thing can exist alone, isolated from the community of life that surrounds it, and the study of how a region's climate, soil, water, plants and animals are interwoven into an interdependent and all-embracing web, each in some way influencing the others, is *ecology*.

Every species of plant and animal has its individualistic range of climatic and habitat requirements to which it has adapted during the evolutionary process and outside of which it cannot survive. Thus a specialized ecological environment like the west coast region acts as an invisible cage, keeping its endemic species in, and keeping many other species out. As a result there are numerous plants, trees, birds and mammals confined to the coast that can live nowhere else in Canada; and numerous others that occur almost everywhere else in Canada *except* here.

Some well-known plant, shrub and tree endemics of the coast are: western sword fern, the common rain-forest fern; Pacific dogwood, B.C.'s floral emblem; salal, an abundant shrub of the rain-forest; Sitka spruce; and at least six additional trees– yellow cedar, amabilis fir, arbutus, Garry oak, broad-leaf maple and vine maple.

As would be expected, there are numerous species of sea-

A natural barrier of rock, ice and snow separates the Pacific coast from the rest of Canada.

birds and shorebirds that occur only along the coast, but a number of land birds too are restricted to the coastal zone and turn up inland only as rare stragglers. Examples are band-tailed pigeon, northwestern crow, common bushtit, Hutton's vireo and the black-throated grey warbler.

Mammals show the same coastal separation. Several species of moles, shrews and voles, the spotted skunk, aplodontia or mountain beaver, Vancouver marmot, Townsend chipmunk and the chickaree or Douglas squirrel are all western U.S. mammals whose ranges extend into Canada only as slender, northward-reaching colonies along the southern B.C. coast or on Vancouver Island. Several other mammals with extensive ranges in western Canada, in some cases all across Canada, have Pacific coast populations that have been altered into distinctive subspecies or races by geographical isolation and the different

environment west of the Coast Mountains. Examples of these are the coast deer, a smaller, darker subspecies of the mule deer; the Roosevelt elk, a Vancouver Island race, larger and darker than the typical inland form; and coastal subspecies of the pika, long-tailed vole, white-footed or deer mouse, marten and snowshoe hare.

These then are some of the more prominent members of the exclusive west coast club—species that in one way or another need the maritime influence that only the Pacific-facing slope or islands can provide.

Yet perhaps the Pacific coast's "apartness" is more strikingly illustrated by what its invisible cage keeps out, rather than by what it keeps in. Among trees, for example, the white spruce and trembling aspen have such wide climatic and soil tolerances that they are abundant everywhere in Canada where trees can grow—except on the Pacific coast. Their ranges start at the Atlantic and extend to the Arctic and Alaska, but except for a few struggling and insignificant clumps of aspen on Vancouver Island the ranges cut off abruptly at the inland slopes of the Coast Mountains. Many plants and shrubs also grow widely throughout Canada but are absent or very rare on the west coast, among them sumach, poison ivy and red raspberry. Birds in the same category are the black-capped chickadee which reaches the coast only around the lowlands of the Fraser River near Vancouver, the common crow which occurs everywhere in Canada except west of the Coast Mountains, and the bank swallow, northern waterthrush and redstart. One of the most familiar and widespread Canadian mammals, the meadow mouse, spans Canada except the northern-most Arctic, but its range stops strikingly a hundred miles or so short of the Pacific. The lynx, wide-ranging too, though much rarer, similarly avoids the coast.

The Pacific coast is distinctive not just for North America, but in a worldwide sense as well. Its original forest of huge coniferous trees, known as "temperate rain forest," is a rarity that has evolved in response to specialized growth conditions in few other temperate-zone areas of the world. Major requirements for creation of a temperate rain forest are persistent winds blowing across a broad expanse of warm sea and a mountainous coast that deflects the winds upward, thus chilling them and abruptly reducing their moisture-holding capacity and forcing them to release their vapour in the form of heavy rains. Since prevailing winds in the earth's temperate zones are from the west, only westward-facing mountainous coasts fill these requirements.

Similar temperate rain forests are found only on the Pacific slope of the Andes in southern Chile which is South America's counterpart of North America's northwest coast, in limited regions of Japan because of winds off the East China Sea and the Sea of Japan, and on the western coast of New Zealand. The North American Pacific coast forest from its southern anchor in the redwoods and sequoias of northern California to its Sitka spruce of Alaska, though most of its big primeval stands are now gone, is still the world's finest and most extensive surviving example of a temperate rain forest.

Though a small and distinctive biotic region, it is far from being monotonously uniform. Its unusual linking of mountains and temperate sea gives it a diversity of habitats, and this in turn produces a broad, intriguing spectrum of living forms. Its mountains rise in many places directly from the sea, so often within a few miles there is the whole exciting gamut of life zones from sea-bottom and intertidal mud, through tropic-like rain forest, to stunted sub-alpine forest, to alpine meadows, and finally at the mountain-top, Arctic-type tundra. This means that species normally spread out across a couple of thousand miles of latitude are here compressed into the span of a one-day hike by the rapidly altering life zones that result from changing altitudes. In most places one goes north to reach the Arctic, but in mountainous country like this one goes up.

The life spectrum starts offshore with the aquatic life of the dark and hidden world under the sea. The main life forms here, of course, are the fishes, a prodigious array of them, conventional ones like the five species of salmon, but also a host of grotesque, fascinating, many-shaped and many-coloured weirdies —skates up to eight feet long which fly through the water instead of swim; the grunt sculpin that creeps on the bottom using its fins as legs; the pipefish that stands on its tail to look like a blade of undersea grass, and a multitude of others. Sharing the same undersea habitat are jellyfish, squids, octopuses and the large marine mammals—whales, dolphins, porpoises, seals and sea-lions.

The inshore kelp jungles and tideswept rocks and mudflats is yet another world. Here a different and new horde of clinging, crawling, burrowing creatures—sponges, sea anemones, worms, starfish, sea urchins, sea cucumbers, limpets, clams, snails, oysters, barnacles, sand fleas, shrimps and crabs—live bizarre and sedentary lives. Each has its own system for surviving in this punishing environment of hammering surf and the intermittent ebb and flow of tides. And over the ocean are great flocks of seabirds, denizens of the air, but with lifeways that tie them inexorably to the sea.

Ashore, the plant sequence runs from prickly pear cactus on the balmy lowlands of the Gulf Islands near Victoria to the creeping Arctic willow and tundra heaths of the mountain summits. Animal species range from hummingbirds and wood warblers, whose ancestral origins were tropical, to Arctic and high-altitude forms such as ptarmigans, lemmings, mountain goats and that strangest of all living organisms—the ice worm that inhabits mountain-top glaciers. No other part of Canada has such abundant and varied life in so limited an area, or so many endemic species that it can claim as exclusively its own. A naturalist's Eden, it is indeed a land apart.

2 THE LOOK OF THE LAND

The crowded summer cruise ships plying the Inside Passage from Vancouver to Alaska have turned it into one of the most "looked at" coasts in the world, and with good reason, for if it isn't the world's most beautiful coast it certainly has only a couple of other contenders for the honour. Yet except for its southernmost 150 miles, it is sparsely settled, still in a relatively pristine state, and rarely penetrated or even visited by the deck-bound tourists sailing past its mountains and fiords.

The northern 400 miles of the Canadian section has no coastal roads and only three major communities the pulpmill centre of Ocean Falls, the aluminum-smelting town of Kitimat, and the northern port of Prince Rupert. Otherwise, man's tenure on this coast is restricted to a sprinkling of small, widely spaced fishing ports, logging camps and Indian villages, most of them hidden far inside the twisting fiords.

The region has a baffling nature mystery that emphasizes how little is known about this coast region. One of its commonest birds is the marbled murrelet, a little seabird that can be seen in flocks of hundreds, yet because of dense coastal forests and inaccessible terrain, and despite decades of searching, definite evidence of where and how it nests has never been found.

If we look at the coast, not as the cruise-ship tourist sees it, but from the vantage point of a Seattle-to-Anchorage plane, the first major land feature that will appear as our northbound plane reaches cruising altitude over the Strait of Georgia will be the flat lowlands of southern Vancouver Island to the left and the broad plain of the Fraser River Delta on the mainland to the right. Blocked off in rectangular fields, lined with highways, railroads and transmission lines, and spotted with towns, this would be a conventional and unremarkable region of farms and urban sprawl in most parts of Canada, but it stands out strikingly here from the forested, mountainous, up-and-down terrain that surrounds it.

The mainland portion, the Fraser Lowland, is a triangle with sides 50 to 70 miles long, its base extending along the coast from Vancouver south to Bellingham, Washington, and its apex at Hope on the Fraser River. It is the result of 60 million years of sediment deposition by the Fraser River which rises near the Alberta border and loops for 850 miles through the B.C. interior before reaching the sea. The Fraser is still extending its delta shelf out under the Strait of Georgia at a rate of 28 feet a year.

The Pacific dogwood, black-throated grey warbler, and mountain beaver are all confined to the Pacific coast.

Because of mild climate, abundant rainfall and rich alluvial soils, the Fraser Lowland is the most productive farming area of British Columbia—a distinction it may not retain, for it is being rapidly engulfed by Vancouver's urban sprawl.

This flat southern corner of the mainland and Vancouver Island is the coast's only extensively settled agricultural area and, except for one small pocket 250 miles to the north around Bella Coola, it is the only coastal region where agriculture is possible.

B.C.'s two main cities, Vancouver and Victoria, and two-thirds of the province's population are here, and the flat stretches of agricultural soil that surround them are only part of the reason. More significantly the canyon which the Fraser River cut through the Coast Mountains in its long geological history provided the easiest rail route to tidewater when the first transcontinental railway was pushed through to the coast. Burrard Inlet, which forms the north boundary of the Fraser Lowland, was a natural end-of-steel harbour. Thus Vancouver was born, and the province's commercial and industrial development concentrated here in this southwestern corner.

Undoubtedly enticements of climate and geology have also attracted population, for Victoria's balmy Mediterranean-type climate and Vancouver's rugged geographical setting make them very pleasant places to live. Vancouver, with the green gem of Stanley Park in its heart, and its backdrop of snow-flecked mountains, has the most beautiful setting of any North American city.

A spatter of rocky, irregular islands dot the Strait of Georgia between Vancouver and Victoria. These, the Gulf Islands, are linked by a network of ferries, and the larger ones have limited farming. They are of special interest to naturalists because they are nesting sites for isolation-seeking seabirds. Some plants, notably the prickly pear cactus, which are becoming rare elsewhere on the coast, are still abundant here.

As we move northwestward up the Strait of Georgia, the mountains close in, pinching off the broad southern lowlands until they are only narrow strips along each side of the strait. On the mainland side, the first fiords appear immediately north of Vancouver, their sinuous, blue ribbons cutting deep into the mountains that surround them. The fiords make a continuous coastal road impossible. For the first 90 miles north of Van-couver, there are broken stretches of road linked by ferries that cross the fiords, but there the mainland route ends.

The inside, eastern coast of Vancouver Island is more hospitable. Here the Coastal Trough that forms the Strait of Georgia has an upper rim that has risen above sealevel to produce a flat, narrow, well-soiled shelf known as the Nanaimo Lowland. There are no great fiords on this side of the island, as there are on the mainland opposite, and thus Vancouver Island's main highway is here, running 210 miles up the island from Victoria through Nanaimo and Campbell River to end at Kelsey Bay. There are farmlands along this coastal ribbon, but they are concentrated in pockets around towns with stretches of forest between.

But all this is mountain country, and its patches of flat lowland, its blue ribbons of fiords and even the 20-mile-wide swath of the Strait of Georgia up which our plane is flying are puny intrusions into the sweeping, rumpled panorama of mountains that reaches to the horizon on all sides.

The Vancouver Island Ranges, which cover almost all the island, are lower and more rounded than the mainland mountains opposite. Few of them rise above 7,000 feet, but they are rugged and cut by deep valleys. Some of the valleys extend completely across the island and dip below sealevel to terminate as fiords on the west coast facing the open Pacific, making this outer shore another fiord-shredded and island-dotted coast like the mainland.

Because of Vancouver Island's interior mountain barrier, practically all of its precipitous, fiorded west coast is isolated, its sprinkling of fishing ports and logging towns reached only by sea. The island has a considerable network of company-owned logging roads but few of them are open to the public. There is only one public road that crosses the island and provides access to its outer Pacific coast—a road about a third of the way up the island that runs from Parksville to the outer coast towns of Tofino and Ucluelet. This is the picturesque Long Beach area where both the provincial and national governments are establishing large seaside parks.

Long Beach has been recently designated as a National Park. Sand beaches like this are a rarity on the mountainous coastline of B.C.

Two-thirds of the way up Vancouver Island the Strait of Georgia below us is blocked by an archipelago of islands, and Vancouver Island becomes separated from the mainland only by a chaotic network of narrow channels.

From this point on communities are few, but there are frequent reminders that man is here as an itinerant harvester of the coast's resources. There are rafts of logs clogging river-mouth booming grounds, tugs towing barges and log booms, and the small white specks of fishing craft trailing silver wakes behind them.

But there is another more subtle sign that man has been almost everywhere along the coast. The forest of most mountainsides has a sharp, horizontal line a third or halfway up with the forest dark green above this line and a softer green below. The upper, darker segments are the original forest of mature, spire-like conifers; the lower sections have had the original forest cut away by loggers and it has grown in with second-growth forest of deciduous species like red alder and maple which give it the lighter colour. The location of the line is the point at which the slope became too steep for further logging, or where the trees decreased in size because of the growth limitations of higher altitudes. But in some places there is no soft green pastel of new forest coming in where the old was logged; instead there are bare rocks or gullied hillsides clothed only with scraggly patches of bushes—stark indictments of heedless, cut-and-get-out logging methods that made no provisions for reforestation, leaving soil to be flushed away by rains and runoff, producing wastelands that may never grow trees again.

Our flight path takes us past the northern end of Vancouver Island, out over the Pacific. There is only the mainland coast in sight now, on our right. We have already seen numerous fiords along the coast behind us, but now they coalesce to produce a coast dissected into a maze of channels and islands, desolate, hostile, but majestically beautiful. "Fiord," incidentally, is a term not widely used here except by geologists; instead they are variously called "inlets," "channels," "arms," sounds," and even "canals." But they are classic fiords in every respect—narrow, steep walled, with abrupt, often right-angle turns, and deep

Timber rafts pinpoint the location of a lumber mill — a familiar sight along the Pacific coast.

water navigable for large ships. They rank in size and scenic grandeur with the world-famed fiords of Norway, Patagonia and New Zealand. Silver ribbons of waterfalls cascade down their sides, and frequently there are bare gashes of rock where land-slides have plunged down the steep slopes sweeping away the forest. The fiords are indicators of a "drowned" coastline, for they were created when the sea flowed into glacial-cut valleys as the glaciers melted back. From here to the Gulf of Alaska an unbroken labyrinth of fiords will be unrolling like a tattered carpet beneath us, so continuous and interlocking that in the 1,000-mile Inside Passage route from Vancouver to Skagway there arc only two brief stretches totalling 50 miles where ships have to leave sheltered water and venture onto the open Pacific.

The Queen Charlottes appear on the Pacific horizon a hundred and twenty miles northwest of Vancouver Island. This massive block of islands is sparsely settled. It doesn't hug the coast as Vancouver Island does, permitting easy ferry access, but instead it sits out on the edge of the Continental Shelf with the stormy, 60-mile moat of Hecate Strait separating it from the mainland. It is a wedge-shaped group of islands tapering to an attenuated point at the southern end, but 180 miles ahead at its northern end it broadens to a width of 60 miles.

Its backbone is the Queen Charlotte Ranges, low by the mountain standards of this coast. Few of the peaks rise more than 3,500 feet, because their foundations are deep under the sea and only their upper portions are visible. But, though low, many of the peaks are sharp and ice-sculptured, for the Ice-Age glaciers this far out at sea were thinner and didn't plane off the mountain tops as occurred on the mainland peaks of the same elevation.

The mountain range forms a narrow bulwark along the western, outer coast, and the broadening of the island wedge that becomes apparent about halfway up its length is created by a flat lowland reaching eastward from the mountains. Lowlands are rare on this coast, and this is an extensive one, forming a triangle with about sixty miles to a side. There hasn't been a comparable lowland plain since the Fraser Lowland almost 500 miles south. But this one is still more remarkable for it has a silver strand of beach along its eastern shore. Beaches on this Pacific coast are even rarer than coastal lowlands, because its rock is resistant to wave erosion, producing little sand, and in most places the shoreline plunges steeply into deep water, leaving no shelves for beach production.

The few beaches are lonely and little-known for there are few people here to enjoy them. Only about 3,000 people live on the Queen Charlottes, half of them Indians, and most in small settlements along the coast of this northeastern lowland. The local industries that support them are fishing and logging. The climate is suitable for farming, but the lowland soils are highly acid and require costly draining, with the result that in the almost 4,000 square miles of the Queen Charlottes there are only about 500 acres of cultivated cropland—the equivalent of one good prairie farm.

The remote cliffs and islets of the Queen Charlottes form the major nesting region for some species of seabirds that rarely nest elsewhere, and the islands are the last big refuge of the dramatic peregrine falcon, a bird that is disappearing everywhere on the continent except here.

The Queen Charlottes are also the subject of an interesting controversy between biologists and geologists as to whether the islands were completely covered by the Pleistocene ice sheet. Biologists contend that a number of Queen Charlotte plants and animals are distinct species or subspecies so different from their mainland relatives that they must have been isolated from the mainland ancestral stocks for a much longer period than the relatively brief 10,000 years that have passed since the last Ice Age. They say that the Queen Charlotte weasel, marten, black bear and dusky shrew show differences so great that they would require something in the order of 100,000 years to evolve, not 10,000. This would require the existence of unglaciated refuges on the Queen Charlottes where they could have survived the Ice Age *in situ* instead of migrating back to the islands at the Ice Age's end. But geologists insist that the geological evidence indicates the Queen Charlottes were completely covered with glaciers; or at most only a few highest peaks could have remained above the ice as nunataks which would have been swept so harshly by gales and snowslides that no animals or even plants could have survived on them.

Our plane flies on. The mist-dimmed, legendary Queen Charlottes fall behind. Prince Rupert, which became the coast's second transcontinental rail terminus in 1914 when the Grand Trunk Pacific chose the Skeena River route through the Coast

Mountains, passes on the mainland to our right. It is an important port, pulpmill and fish-processing site, and the only city on this northern coast.

Now Alaska is just ahead, and our flight path takes us over the Panhandle's archipelago of channels and islands. The Alaskan Panhandle is more than 100 miles wide, so the summits of the Boundary Ranges which form the interior border with B.C. are only a distant, white pimpling on the inland horizon. Because we are approaching the subarctic, thousands of square miles here are permanently covered with ice and snow. In fact, the Boundary Range summits at this southern end of the Alaskan Panhandle are the beginning of an almost-continuous ridge of icefields that arcs in a great white scimitar for 1,000 miles around the Gulf of Alaska to the Aleutians. Though the movement of these glaciers is so slow that only careful study can detect it, they are acually flowing rivers of ice. By the time ice reaches sealevel and finally melts it can be several centuries old. These mountain icefields can be regarded as lingering remnants of the Ice Age which are still melting back, for some of the glacial ice-fronts are receding at a rate of close to 100 feet a year.

Three hundred and fifty miles up the Alaskan Panhandle looms a new towering jumble of mountains dwarfing the peaks around them. And this is B.C. again, for here the northwestern corner of the province extends westward across the upper end of the Panhandle, bringing a small wedge of Canadian terrain beneath us briefly one more.

This corner where Alaska, Yukon and British Columbia meet is the ridgepole of Canada. Its craggy, obdurate, soaring complex of peaks, known as the St. Elias Mountains, rise from the sea in a great, white, serrated wall, the loftiest and most rugged mountain range on the continent. Several of these peaks are 15,000 to 19,000 feet high, culminating in 19,850-foot Mount Logan on the Yukon side, the highest peak in Canada, and the highest in North America except for 20,300-foot Mount McKinley farther north in Alaska.

The Canadian portion of our Seattle-to-Anchorage flight ends here as we fly on into Alaska. Look back and the last fragment of Canada we see will be the gnarled, snow-stippled mass of Mount Logan towering over the Alaskan peaks around it long after all else Canadian has disappeared.

Mount Logan has another distinction. The Pacific coast runs northwestward, not truly northward, so Mount Logan on the Yukon border also marks Canada's most western extremity. A line extended down the Pacific coast southward would end up 600 miles west of Vancouver Island. With this geographical picture in mind, let's visualize the ending of a Canadian summer day.

The dark crescentic shadow of night, pushing a crimson ribbon of sunset before it, sweeps in off the Atlantic and touches Newfoundland first. Night settles on the Maritimes, but the Yukon 3,000 miles away is in its early afternoon. The line of night races westward faster than a jet plane's flight. Three hours later it is crossing the prairies; four hours later it is bringing dusk to Vancouver. But because of the longer day of northern latitudes and the northwestward lay of the coast, sunset comes to the Queen Charlottes an hour or two later than to Vancouver, and to the southwestern Yukon three or four hours later. Finally, however, the night shadow crosses the Yukon border and moves westward across Alaska. But there is a fragment of Canada that has not yet relinquished its hold on the retreating day, for 19,850-foot Mount Logan is still thrusting its craggy pinnacle up into the sunset's crimson glow.

During the preceding eight hours, more than twenty million Canadians have seen daylight wane and night come. Back in the Maritimes where it began, it is almost time for another dawn. But here where the Canadian day will have its dying moments, there is probably no one within sight to see its final snuffing out, because the largest glacier mass of the continent fans out across a couple of thousand square miles around Mount Logan's base.

The shadow line creeps up the mountain's westward face like a guillotine. Logan is mostly snow and ice, with only black ribs of rock protruding here and there, so there are no stunted trees, no green pockets of alpine meadow to soften the sunset's glare as it is pushed to the mountain's summit. The waning rays flare up for the last minutes of crimson alpenglow on the topmost fields of dazzling snow; in their final seconds they shimmer hesitantly as though reluctant to go, and then fade suddenly to grey.

Throughout most of the year, except for midwinter, this is the pattern of Canada's sunsets. And here atop Mount Logan's icy crest the Canadian day finally dies.

A LOOK AT THE COASTLINE

The Pacific coast of Canada is famous for its rugged beauty of wild surf
and soaring mountains, its mild marine climate, unique plant and animal life, wealth of natural
resources, and its close links with the all-embracing, ever present sea.

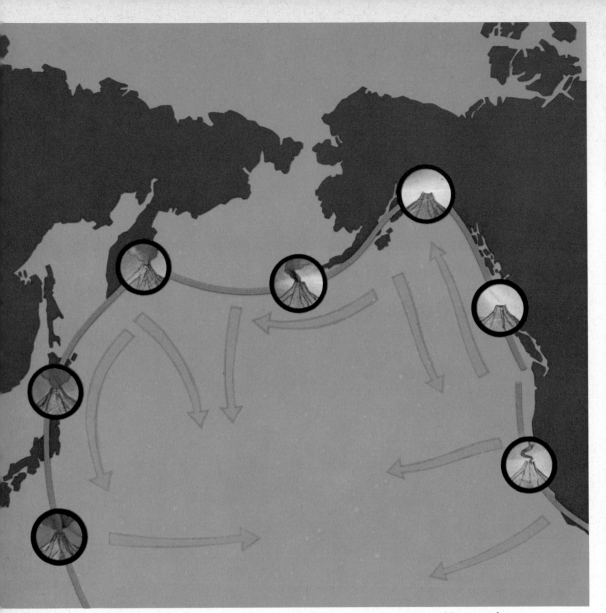

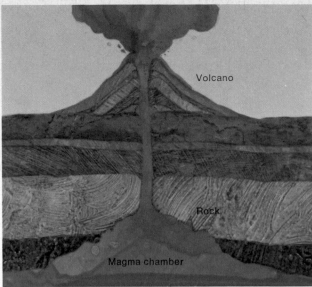

The Pacific Ocean is ringed by about 300 active volcanoes and its margins are rocked by frequent earthquakes. The arrows above indicate the directions of the shifting crustal movements that produce these earthquakes.

Volcanoes extrude lava from within the earth's crust. Erosion later exposes the hard volcanic cores.

The Ring of Fire

The area around the North Pacific Ocean is often called the Ring of Fire because of its heavy volcanic activity and its many earthquakes. The earthquakes result from the shifting of the position of the continents with respect to the ocean basin, as suggested by the arrows in the first diagram. The major coastal volcano areas are also noted; those on the British Columbia

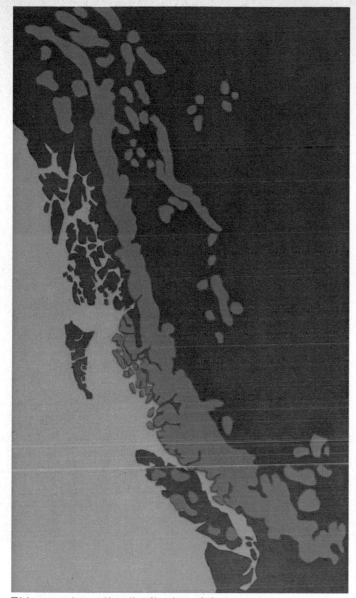

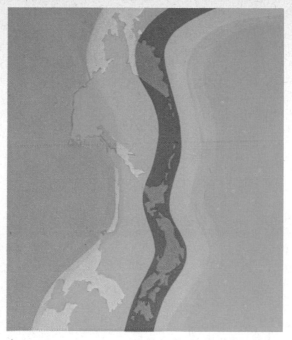

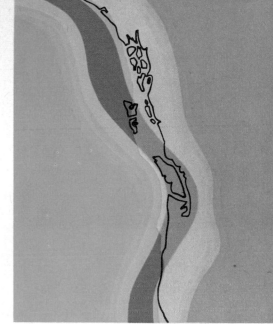

This map shows the distribution of the Coast Range Batholith which was formed about 120 million years ago.

The west coast of North America, 250 million years ago (top right), is believed to have looked like the Asian Pacific coast of today (top left). The diagram (bottom) shows a cross-section of the Pacific floor with its major fault zones.

coast are currently inactive. There are active volcanoes all along the other sections of the ring as well as in Hawaii. The Coast Range Mountains bordering the Pacific coast are volcanic in origin and date from the time when this area of the Ring of Fire was active. The formations we see today are ancient magma intrusions exposed when tens of millions of years of erosion wore away any softer surrounding rock. A detailed study of the rocks of the east and west shores of the Pacific suggest that the geography of Japan today bears great resemblance to that of the British Columbia coast 250 million years ago. The volcanoes in Japan are currently active and much of the erosion that characterizes the British Columbia coast has not yet occurred.

Diatryma

Eohippus

Palaeosyops

Notharctus

Eocene life fleeing from a volcano

Twenty million years ago, earth movements produced a widespread withdrawal of inland seas. The Tertiary period, of which the Eocene formed the second epoch, was a time of great volcanic activity and mountain building in North America. Intensive volcanism covered hundreds of thousands of square miles with lava flows and ash falls which intermingled with various water and wind deposited sediments. Lava flows were especially numerous in the Columbia and Snake River valleys where dozens of individual flows, alternating with soils and plant remains, reach a total thickness of 5,000 to 6,000 feet. A period of generally mild climate, the Eocene saw the rise of many more advanced plant and animal species. Flowering plants became a dominant feature during this period. The primitive ancestor of the horse, the Eohippus, also first appeared at this time. Side by side with a large number of marine invertebrates lived an ever increasing quantity of fishes similar to those of the present day. The great reptiles were replaced by birds and by mammals whose constant blood temperatures made them less vulnerable to climate variations.

Ice

Sea Level

Ice

1: One million years ago. The Ice Age begins.

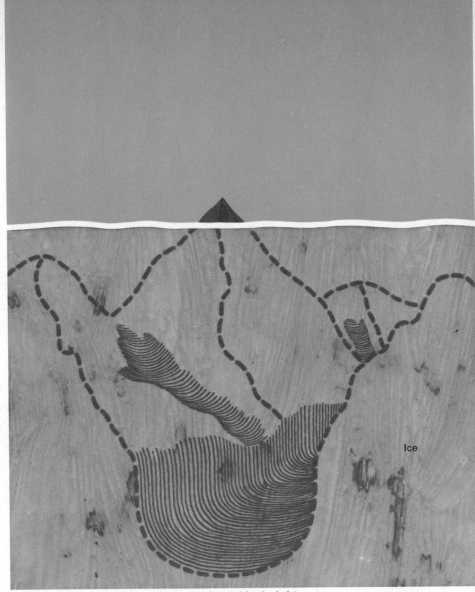

Ice

2: Twenty thousand years ago. Ice Age at its height.

Under gouging ice

A fiord is the result of a million years of gouging ice, followed by a flooding invasion of the sea. A V-shaped river valley (1) fills with rasping ice, which begins enlarging the fiord and creating a U-shaped profile. The background mountains have been rounded by millions of years of erosion. At the height of the Ice Age (2), ice covers everything except the highest peak which is sharpened as ice carves out its sides. The main valley is greatly deepened, but its tributary valleys are not, and they retain their original, higher level.

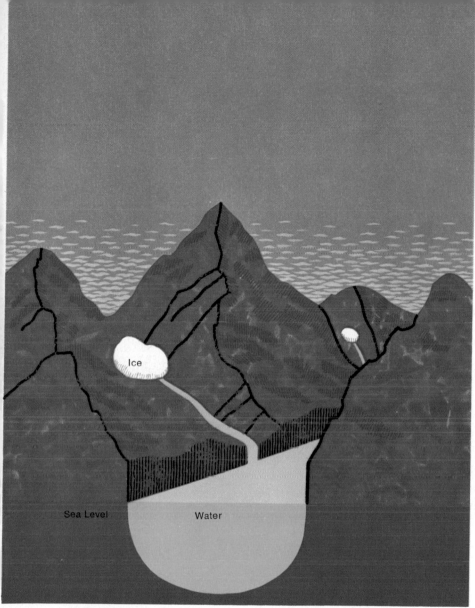

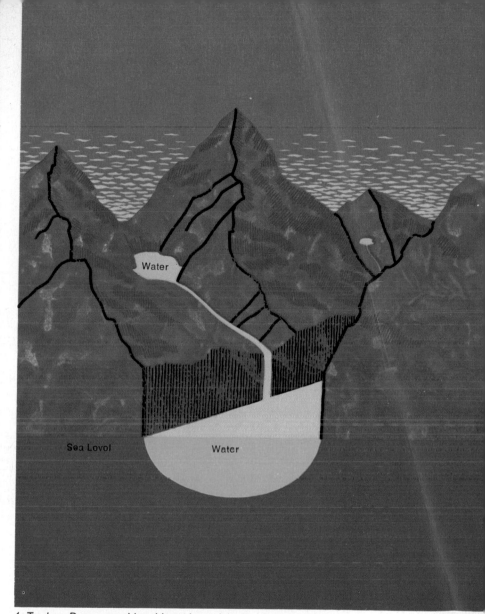

3: Ten thousand years ago. Ice has melted, sea returned.

4: Today. Depressed land has risen, but fiord remains.

The ice sheet has flowed far out over the ocean bottom, and its massive weight has caused the land to sag several hundred feet. The ice sheet has melted (3) and only remnants of glaciers remain at high, colder altitudes. The sea has returned to its preglacial shoreline. The sea has flooded the gouged out river valley, turning it into a fiord. But the land responds slowly to the release from the great weight of ice it carried. It is still depressed in relation to sea level, and the fiord is flooded more deeply than it will be later.

Today (4) the high mountainside glaciers have melted and become alpine lakes. The sagging land and ocean bottom have rebounded to perhaps their preglacial level, although it is not known for sure whether the Pacific coast has reached its preglacial equilibrium, or whether it is still in the process of rising. The elevation of the land has spilled water out of the fiord, making it shallower, and giving it higher walls. The undeepened tributary stream pours down the fiord wall as a waterfall and is known as a "hanging valley."

Glacial lakes were formed by the retreating glaciers.

The rocky shore

The Pacific coast provides some of the most beautiful scenery in Canada. Many of the land formations in these photographs were caused by the last glacial advance which ended about 10,000 years ago. The advancing ice deepened the fiords while, at the same time, lowering the whole coastline under its immense weight. With the retreat of the glacial ice and the resulting rebounding of the land to its natural level, many glacial lakes and hanging valleys were left stranded high above the present water level.

far left: Bottleneck Inlet — one of many coastal inlets.

*left: A hanging valley is one of the most interesting and **beautiful geological phenomena** on the coast.*

right: This typical coastal inlet and offshore islands are covered with lush timber growth.

For the Nootka sea-hunters, fiords were natural whale traps

The rugged Nootka of Vancouver Island's western coast were the only Pacific Indians who engaged in the most spectacular and dangerous of all sea hunting — the harpooning of whales. They exploited the unique features of their coast, its fiords, by driving whales into the narrow channels where they could be more easily cornered and killed. Often, however, they challenged the great sea mammals in perilous jousts on the open sea. Nootka boats, designed for whaling with gracefully curved prows and flared sides to repel waves, were the most seaworthy of all Pacific Indian craft. Paddlers tried to approach a whale unobserved from the rear while their harpooner stood poised in the prow. The 20-foot harpoon was too heavy to be thrown; the boat had to be manoeuvred alongside the whale so that the harpoon could be plunged directly into it. A skilled harpooner might cut the tail tendons and leave the whale incapable of swimming, but usually the first strike only wounded the animal. This was the dangerous moment, for the whale's thrashing struggle could smash the boat and seriously injure its crew. The harpoon had a detachable head with a blade of mussel shell and elk horn barbs which came free of the shaft, but a sinew line remained attached to it. As the whale dove, the line snaked out of the boat, sometimes entangling and dragging a crewman with it. Attached to the end of it were large seal skin floats which impeded the whale, preventing it from sounding deeply. The whalers followed the buoys and when the whale surfaced it would be met with another harpoon and more of the dragging floats. When the whale finally lay weakened and exhausted on the surface, a strike with a special lance to the heart would kill it. Then it had to be towed ashore, sometimes from miles out at sea, demanding a day or two of arduous paddling.

Highways to the sea

Lumber is British Columbia's most valuable
natural resource. The coastal forest thrives
in the warm wet climate of the area but
because of the high quality of the timber and
the easy access afforded to loggers by the
sea and numerous rivers the Pacific coast
timber is currently being cut at a rate
three times faster than normal regrowth.
The future of this industry, and the Pacific
coast forest itself, is thus threatened
with eventual extinction unless man adjusts
his harvest of the timber to more closely
approximate nature's ability to replenish the
supply. Once the logs are cut they are trans-
ported over land to the rivers and assembled
into huge floating islands of logs, called log
booms. The log booms are then slowly towed
to mills where they are sorted and converted
into many lumber and paper products.

PART TWO / GEOLOGY

3 THE MOUNTAINS ARE BORN

We may think of scenery, the earth's surface landforms, as being permanent and unchanging. What looks more solid and enduring than a mountain? But mountains are enduring only within the context of the brief span of time that each human generation has in which to observe them. In the eons of geological time, even mountains come and go, rising up inch by inch in response to the buckling of the earth's crust produced by subterranean pressures, and being worn down again in the same slow and relentless way under the eroding forces of ice and water. Rock that formed originally as the compacted mud of a sea bottom may be uplifted to become the mountain crests of a later age, only to be rasped away and carried seaward to end up once again on the sea bottom.

The mountainous and ocean-carved Pacific coast that we see today is but a fragmentary stage in a long history of marine flooding and mountain upheavals which have created dramatic changes of landscape again and again, and which will go on changing it to the end of time.

The crustal squeezing and buckling that produce mountains goes on so slowly that only intricate study can detect them. The presence of sea-life fossils high up on shores from which the sea has long receded are one clue to the lifting of bordering lands. Such studies indicate that some coastal regions of Vancouver Island have been rising at a rate of five feet a century in recent times, but this abnormally rapid uplift is caused by the fact that the coast here was greatly depressed by the weight of Ice-Age glaciers and has been springing back since its ice load melted. The Queen Charlotte Islands, on the other hand, are rising about three inches a century—a more typical example of the rate at which mountain-building processes work.

It is only when uplift is occurring more rapidly than erosion that mountains are born. Rocks vary widely in their resistance to erosion, depending on the hardness of their minerals and the degree of cohesion cementing their rock crystals together. As a result erosion works more rapidly in some spots than others, and it is this interplay of crustal uplift and varying patterns of erosion that carves out the chaotic profiles of peaks, domes, cirques, ridges, terraces, and valleys that comprise typical mountain scenery.

Measuring the extent of the radioactive decay of uranium atoms has shown that the earth's crust is more than three billion years old. During this long and tortured geological history, the region that is now the Pacific coast changed its shape and structure many times, but most of the early record of the rock formations has been destroyed or buried by a long succession of evolutionary cycles. To find the origin of the bedrock that has been sculptured into the B.C. coastal scenery of today, we can begin approximately 150 million years ago during the geological period called the Jurassic.

At that time a shallow, sea-filled trough ran down the edge of the ocean along an offshore island or a long north-south peninsula farther to the west. For millions of years, sediments from the surrounding land and lavas from submarine volcanoes built up on the trough's undersea floor. As this rock accumulated, the floor sagged under its weight, letting the accumulation continue until in places it built up to a depth of 13,000 feet. This interfusion of volcanic and sedimentary deposits is the rock that makes up most of the Vancouver Island and Queen Charlotte mountains of today.

During this same period in the region of today's mainland coast a geologic event was occurring that would determine the character of the bedrock that now forms the Coast Mountains. There were huge upwellings of molten lava here too, but thick cappings of overlying rock kept the lava imprisoned underground. Since the lava was unable to release its tremendous pressure by bursting out onto the surface, it built up in a gigantic subsurface blister that cooled slowly into a mass of granite thousands of feet thick, 100 miles wide, and 1,100 miles long, stretching from the Canadian border to Alaska. This is the Coast Range Batholith that was later uncovered by erosion, emerging as the rock that forms the Coast Mountains and virtually all of the mainland coast today. The intense heat and pressures associated with its formation produced the sorting and concentrating of minerals that created many of the rich ore veins now mined in this region.

Mountains produced during this Jurassic period were slowly eroded away, and the region became flat again. Then, about 60 million years ago, in what is known as the Tertiary period, another era of crustal squeezing and unrest once more raised twin chains of mountains along the coast. These chains developed along the site of today's Insular and Coast Mountains, and a downward warping of the crust between them was filled by sea water, producing a trough that corresponds with the present Coastal Trough. Thus except for slight alterations the Pacific coast had assumed its basic modern form.

As this Tertiary squeeze relaxed and its mountain-building ended, the forces of erosion went to work once more. For 45 million years they worked without any new crustal uplifts to offset their levelling process, baring the great blister of the Coast Range Batholith to its granite core, and pouring sediments into the ancestral Coastal Trough to produce the sedimentary rock strata which now underly and account for the flatness of the Fraser Lowland and the lowlands of the northern portion of the Queen Charlotte Islands. By 13 million years ago the coast region was again worn down to a fairly flat plateau.

Approximately 10 to 12 million years ago, the final big uplifting squeeze began. The coast region once more folded along the same three "hinge" lines that it had some 50 million years before: two upward folds along the Insular and Coast Mountains and the downward fold of the Coastal Trough between.

Inch by inch, millenium after millenium, it went on, reviving the old, erosion-flattened Insular Mountains of Vancouver Island and the Queen Charlottes and the Coast Mountains of the mainland. The land rose more or less as a single unit, instead of rising in the chaos of ridges and peaks that mountains always show. However, the ridges and peaks developed through the gouging out of valleys and canyons by rivers.

The Coast Range Batholith is a uniform, homogeneous mass of granite without joints or layers, and it produced humpy, dome-like mountains rather than the layered, sedimentary rocks of the Rockies farther east which could split and tilt in huge angular blocks.

It isn't clear whether the uplift which began about 10 million years ago has ended or whether it is still going on. The uncertainty is due to the fact that one million years ago a new, vastly disrupting geological event took over: the Pleistocene Ice Age. There is plenty of evidence that the Pacific coast has been rising in modern times, but the crust was so depressed by the great weight of the ice sheet that it is difficult to determine whether the current rising of the land is still part of the ancient uplift or if it is due entirely to the springing back of the crust following the melting of the glaciers in the geological yesterday of just 10,000 years ago. We are still too close to it to tell.

When the deep freeze of the Pleistocene epoch began, the Pacific coast looked quite different from today. The mountains, which despite the 10-million-year carving by rivers which they had undergone, were rounder, smoother, with gentler slopes, and narrower, shallower river valleys. The coast itself was more regular, without its shattered fringe of islands and twisting maze of fiords.

This was the scene of one million years ago, a rather austere, undramatic landscape of modest mountains and conventional shore awaiting its face-lifting of ice.

4 THE BIG ICE

Four times during the past million years a quarter or more of the earth's surface has been covered with great, flowing, grinding, one- to two-mile-thick sheets of ice which crept outward from the Arctic.

It doesn't require extreme cold to produce an Ice Age. All that is needed is a heavy snowfall over an appreciably large region that provides a little more snow each winter than can melt the following summer. Year by year and inch by inch, the snow piles up until its weight compacts the lower levels into ice. Eventually, when the ice sheet is thick enough, the ice becomes elastic under its tremendous pressure and starts flowing outward. Another Ice Age is underway.

The massive sheets of ice and the huge flows of water produced on melting profoundly changed the landscape and left behind obvious evidences of glaciation wherever they had been. Gouges and scratches on rock surfaces, called *striae*, indicate the direction in which the ice moved. Boulders carried hundreds of miles can be traced back to the regions of mother rock where the glaciers wrenched them loose, revealing the routes followed by the spreading ice sheets. Vast quantities of rock and sand that the glaciers scooped up and carried along with them were deposited in a complex variety of gravel beds, outwash plains, and characteristically-shaped moraine hills, all of which reveal facts about the passage and chronology of the ice. Each of the four ice advances more or less wiped the slate clean, however, obscuring most of the signs left by preceding advances, so that only the last one can be reconstructed in detail.

North America had two main centres of ice accumulation: Labrador Centre east of Hudson Bay and Keewatin Centre west of it. From these centres the ice pressed outward in a pattern of coalescing lobes, blanketing the Arctic islands of the far north. It moved eastward to the Atlantic, southward across the Great Lakes region, and westward to the eastern rim of the Rockies. But the Keewatin ice sheet failed to push its lobes through the Rockies into the mountain region. Instead, the mountain country produced a formidable ice cap of its own, known today as the Cordilleran Centre.

Because of its mountain terrain, the cycle of ice formation here was different from that of Canada's interior. There, the ice built up in two widespreading, cohesive mounds on relatively flat land and spread out like pancake batter on a griddle; here, it formed as a network of slender mountaintop and valley glaciers that slowly expanded and merged into one great ice cap.

The mountain glaciation started with the formation of small glaciers near the tops of peaks. These are known as *cirque glaciers,* and the amphitheatre-like basins they gouge out of mountainsides just below the peaks are called *cirques.* This gouging out of mountainsides by the advancing ice is what produces the sharp, pyramid-form summits.

As the cirque glaciers enlarged and flowed downward, they combined into valley glaciers which chewed out the mountain bases, further steepening the sides, and widened and deepened the valleys, changing their V-shaped river-cut profiles into the broad U-shapes characteristic of glacial valley erosion. Since ice accumulated faster than the valley glaciers could carry it down to lower altitudes or to the sea, the ice tongues filled the valleys, backed up mountainsides, and joined to become mountain ice caps. Finally, the chains of mountain ice caps spread out and combined into one gigantic regional ice sheet that covered everything but the highest peaks.

Boulders and gravel frozen in the ice turned it into an enormous sheet of sandpaper which ground down everything it passed over. Thus peaks that protruded through the ice were sharpened because the glaciers carved out their sides, whereas peaks which were covered by ice were rasped down and rounded.

In some areas, beds of gravel and rock debris deposited when the glaciers melted lie one atop another, and differing degrees of their weathering indicate that they were left at widely separated times. As a result of such evidence, it has been deduced that there were only two major advances and retreats of the Cordilleran sheet, not four as elsewhere in Canada. But only the last advance, known here as the Vashon glaciation, has left a clear record.

Throughout geological time the Pacific coast was covered many times by ocean water. The shaded portions on the accompanying maps illustrate the position of the land during each geologic era. During the Ordovician almost the entire coast was covered by the sea. By the Cretaceous the sea had again risen to inundate the coast. Not until the Miocene (about 25 million years ago) did the present coast emerge from the sea.

 land   water

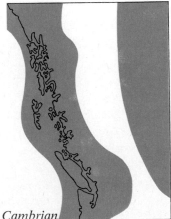
Cambrian

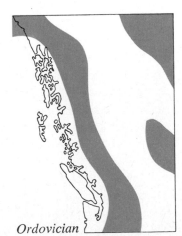
Ordovician

In some respects, the record is more obvious and easier to read in mountain country than in the flatlands of the continent's interior. Peaks that remained above the ice serve as measuring sticks which pinpoint the ice cap's thickness much more accurately than can be done in flat country. It is a fairly simple matter to survey a mountainside for its glacial gouges and ice-transported boulders, and the altitude at which these glacial signs cease is the highest point reached by the ice.

The Cordilleran ice sheet covered a region four to five hundred miles wide and 1,200 miles from north to south. At its maximum extent, its southern edge was a hundred miles south of the Canadian border; its western edge extended out over the Pacific to the outer shores of Vancouver Island and the Queen Charlottes; on the north, it covered most of the Yukon, but only fingers of it extended into Alaska; on the east, it spilled out over foothills and the edge of the prairies.

Much of Alaska remained unglaciated, proof that cold alone did not make the Ice Age. Although Alaska undoubtedly had a cold climate, it apparently escaped the heavy snows which were a more essential Ice Age ingredient.

Evidence left by the Cordilleran sheet's eastern flank along the edge of the prairies provides the chronological record which proves that the mountain region's Ice Age came later than that of the rest of Canada. Here, along a narrow band, deposits left by the Cordilleran sheet overlap deposits of the interior's Keewatin sheet. The Cordilleran carried rocks that can be identified as having come from the B.C. mountains, whereas the Keewatin sediments have rocks that belong to the prairies and the northern interior. As a result, the two deposits are readily separated. The Cordilleran strata are on top, indicating that the mountains' Ice Age reached its maximum after the main continental ice sheets had started melting back.

The thickest Cordilleran ice appears to have built up in the Coast Mountains, probably because of heavier snowfalls near the Pacific. The highest point reached by ice during the last or Vashon glaciation was in the southern end of the Pacific Ranges, a hundred miles or so north of Vancouver, where peaks that protruded through the ice sheet show signs of glaciation to an altitude of 8,700 feet. This means that the ice itself was about 8,000 feet thick over the valley bottoms. The highest ice marks in northern British Columbia stop at around 7,500 feet. Vancouver Island and the Queen Charlottes had lower ice divides—6,300 feet for Vancouver Island and 3,000 feet for Queen Charlottes—because the mountains were lower there, and the climate warmer because of proximity to the Pacific Ocean.

The ice that covered the coastal region came from ice divides in the southern Coast Mountains, the Boundary Ranges, St. Elias Mountains, and the Vancouver Island and the Queen Charlotte Ranges. In the south, ice flowing westward from the mainland and eastward from Vancouver Island met in the Strait of Georgia, filled the strait completely, and then flowed southeastward to the southern end of Vancouver Island where one

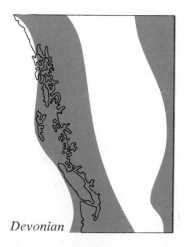

Devonian

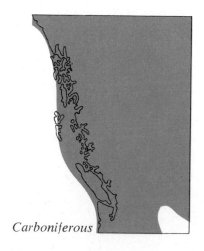

Carboniferous

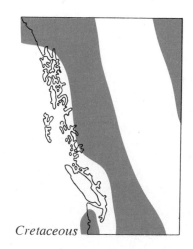

Cretaceous

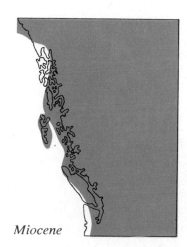

Miocene

lobe pushed into Puget Sound and another turned westward out Juan de Fuca Strait. Farther north, ice from the mainland flowed westward straight across the northern end of Vancouver Island. In Queen Charlotte Sound, north of Vancouver Island, where ocean depths above the continental shelf are mostly 500 feet or less, the mainland ice sheet that was one to two thousand feet thick here probably pushed out across the ocean bottom to at least 50 miles from shore.

In shallower Hecate Strait, westward-moving mainland ice and eastward-pushing Queen Charlotte ice merged in the strait's centre and then turned northward. At the north end of the Queen Charlottes it was blocked by a third ice flow sweeping southward down the Alaskan Panhandle and in the gigantic pushing contest that followed the whole three-pronged confluence of ice welded together and turned westward out Dixon Entrance and along the north coast of the Queen Charlottes. With three great ice centres feeding it, this 30-mile-wide Dixon Entrance tongue probably formed an ice shelf 20 or 30 miles out in the Pacific beyond the Queen Charlottes' western coast to a point where the deepening ocean water would buoy it up off the bottom and keep breaking blocks of it away as icebergs.

The ice fronts pushed bands of Arctic climate ahead of them, producing cool, foggy, rainy summers. Along the Pacific, where moisture-charged winds off the ocean came suddenly over the deep-freeze of ice, the abrupt chilling of the air would instantly reduce its moisture-holding capacity, so that winter was probably one long snowstorm with little respite, and summer a brief interval of almost constant rain and fog.

The Vashon glaciation is believed to have lasted 100,000 years, with a number of minor retreats and advances. Approximately 11,000 years ago, the climate warmed, the heavy snowfalls lessened, and another glacial retreat began. This time the warming has endured to the present day, and no new advance of ice has occurred. In a few thousand years, the Cordilleran ice sheet shrank back through the cycle that had produced it thousands of years before: from regional ice sheet to mountain ice caps to valley glaciers and finally to the cirque glaciers of mountain tops. There are examples of all these stages, except the first one, still surviving today in the high Pacific Ranges of the southern mainland and along the Boundary Ranges into Alaska. All these modern glaciers and icefields are still shrinking, and

though it is customary to regard the Ice Age as having ended 10,000 years ago, it is more accurate to think of these coastal mountains as still emerging from the Ice Age today.

The beginning of the ice recession has been dated by measuring the amount of radioactive carbon in peat and wood from the lowest levels of bog deposits that formed when vegetation began returning behind the retreating ice 11,000 years ago. Since the radioactive portion of carbon contained in all living materials decays to ordinary carbon at a constant rate, the amount of radioactive carbon remaining in any preserved plant sample is a yardstick to determine when the plant grew. Wood samples from some of the earliest postglacial trees to grow on the Fraser River delta indicate an age of 11,300 plus or minus 300. The age of peat from the northern tip of the Queen Charlotte Islands has been established as 10,850 years plus or minus 800 years.

As the ice melted, two factors influenced the shaping of the coastline. First, the level of the sea which had been lowered because of water withdrawn from the ocean to form the glaciers now rose again. Opinions as to how far ocean levels dropped during the Ice Age vary, but the drop was somewhere between 300 and 500 feet. At the same time that the sealevel was reduced, however, the land, especially along the coasts, was sagging under the tremendous weight of its ice load.

A rapid rise in ocean level occurred simultaneously with the melting of the glaciers, but the sagging shores responded more slowly to their release from the ice load they had carried, so slowly, in fact, that the Pacific coast may still be in the process of springing back to its pre-Ice Age level. This meant that there was a period just after the glaciers melted when the ocean level was back to normal but the land was still greatly depressed. During this time, ocean surf and tides beat against shores that have since risen high above the sea. Such old shorelines are recognizable in many places from the remains of ancient beaches, beds of marine clay and gravel, and especially from shells of sea-dwelling mollusks that are now embedded in marine deposits high above present seashores. There are wave-cut terraces indicating that postglacial seas washed against mountainsides north of Vancouver that are now 1,000 feet above sealevel. The eastern side of Vancouver Island has marine deposits 500 feet above the present sea near Campbell

River, sloping down to 300 feet at Victoria; but on the island's west coast, the postglacial uplift has been only about 50 feet.

As the glaciers melted back up the coastal valleys, seawater moved in behind the ice, producing the fiords. There had been a tremendous deepening of all river valleys leading down to the coast because they had served as major drainage outlets for the glaciers, and some had been gouged 2,000 feet below their original preglacial levels during the thousands of years of flowing ice. Nevertheless, deepening was concentrated in the main valleys, not in their smaller, lateral tributaries, and now as the ice wasted away and the sea moved in, the mouths of the undeepened tributary valleys were left as lips, known as *hanging valleys*, high up the side walls of the fiords into which they emptied. Their streams had to cascade hundreds of feet down the fiord walls in waterfalls and this is still a common sight along all fiords today.

Though the ice eventually disappeared and the coastal ends of river valleys were flooded by seawater, the coastline and fiords had not yet acquired the chaotic, labyrinthine outline of today. For a few thousand years, the sea was back to its present-day level while the land remained depressed, so that there was a stage when the fiords were flooded deeper and wider than now, and many of today's coastal islands were still under water. Finally, the tough, granitic, coastal crust, freed of its ice load, rose slowly toward its preglacial equilibrium. The fiord floors lifted to their present constricted, narrow form, lowering the water and only the fact that they had been so overdeepened by the glaciers prevented many of them from spilling dry. Despite this uplift (1,000 feet in the southern mainland) some of the fiords still have water half a mile deep. At the same time, submerged, glacier-rounded mountains off the coast were lifted above the sea to become islands with new networks of channels and fiords between them.

Eventually, the land reached its old level, although it may still be in the final stages of postglacial adjustment. At a period perhaps no more than 5,000 or 6,000 years ago, moments in the geologist's dimensions of time, the Pacific coast had assumed its modern form.

Spectacular rock formations, this one on the Queen Charlotte Islands, support a variety of plant and bird life.

5 THE SHATTERED CLIMATE

Geology gave the land its basic structure and the raw materials for its soil, but it is climate that selects the veneer of vegetation that will grow on the land to give the landscape its finished form. Then vegetation and climate together become the principal selectors of natural history's end product: the wildlife that will inhabit the land.

Climate plays an especially emphatic role on the Pacific coast, for it is climatic features which, more than anything else, form the boundaries of the invisible cage that makes the coast a land apart. Because mountains break the region up into a myriad of small, enclosed pockets with abruptly changing altitudes and varying degrees of exposure to the sea, it is a "shattered" climate, a mosaic of contrasting weather zones. On the whole, it is the wettest climate in Canada, and yet the coast has pockets much drier than the Canadian average, while only 150 miles away in the B.C. interior lies Canada's driest region, parts of which are almost desert. It creates winters so mild and un-Canadian that roses bloom in January on southern Vancouver Island. It changes so radically over short distances that Henderson Lake in southern Vancouver Island averages 264 inches of rainfall a year, whereas Victoria, 75 miles away, has 25 to 30 inches. Summer droughts on the Gulf Islands favour the growth of prickly pear cactus, yet 50 miles to the west there is dripping, tropic-like rain forest, and 70 miles north there is the permanent snow of Mount Garibaldi. Prince Rupert, with an average of 937 hours of sunshine a year, is the cloudiest weather station in Canada; Victoria, with more than 2,200 hours, is one of the sunniest.

The west coast's climate story has its beginning 4,000 miles away, in the torrid equatorial zone of the mid-Pacific. Here, surface water warmed by the tropical sun is pushed westward by the trade winds as the North Equatorial Current. When it reaches the Philippine Islands, the main body of it is deflected northward where it becomes the Kuroshio or Japanese Current. The northeast-to-southwest configuration of Japan and the prevailing westerly winds of the north temperate zone turn it eastward off Japan back toward North America before its tepid,

tropical water can reach the subarctic and be cooled. Now, as the North Pacific Drift, it does a sluggish return flow across the north Pacific.

The significant event in all this, for our west coast climate story, is the fact that the current is steered away from the Arctic, thereby reaching the west coast of Canada and the U.S. while it is still relatively warm. Its surface temperature off British Columbia ranges from 60° Fahrenheit in summer to the middle 40's in winter, making it one of the most effective summer airconditioners and winter hotwater-heating systems in the world.

Thus air masses saturated with moisture from having moved across thousands of miles of warm Pacific are constantly being carried against the west coast by prevailing westerly winds. When the air reaches the coastal mountains, it is deflected upward, and cools at higher altitudes, which reduces its water-holding capacity, and the excess vapour it can no longer carry condenses and is dumped out as snow or rain. Then, when it spills over the top of a mountain range and starts sinking down the eastern slopes, it becomes warmer "thirsty" air, and holds onto its moisture, with the result that the rain or snow clouds clear, and the sun shines again.

Western Canada and the U.S. consist of a series of parallel, north-south-running mountain ranges, so that the eastward-flowing Pacific air is bumped up and down like a roller coaster. Since it has to dump out some of its moisture at each rise it has a little less for the next mountain range. This means that the first bump of the roller coaster, the outer island or coastal range, gets the heaviest precipitation. The precipitation decreases progressively with each inland mountain chain until the air is wrung relatively dry by the time it finally drops down the east side of the Rockies to the Prairies.

Even along the narrow ribbon of coast where the heaviest and most persistent precipitation occurs, however, there is tremendous variation over short distances. This variation is caused by the erratic mountain, valley and fiord profiles. As a result, an annual precipitation map for the coast showing its precipitation belts looks like a crazy quilt of twisted, scalloped ribbons.

Pacific air first flows up against the outer coast of Vancouver Island, producing an annual rainfall of over 100 inches. As the air moves up the westward faces of the Vancouver Island Mountains, rainfall steadily becomes heavier and more fre-

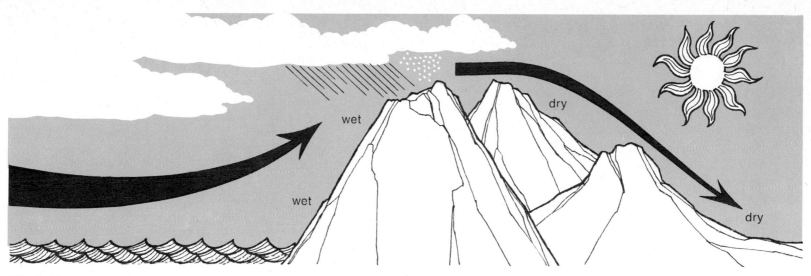

Winds blowing over the warm Pacific absorb huge quantities of moisture; as the air rises to cross the mountains it is cooled and releases the moisture in the form of rain and snow on the west coast.

quent, and there is a high mountaintop belt down the centre of the island which receives 150 to 200 inches a year. Fiords have a funnelling effect, first compressing rain clouds, and then forcing them to rise abruptly at the fiord ends, often producing extremely heavy rainfall in very limited areas. Thus, the vicinity of Ucluelet on the outer coast, though a precipitation map will show it in the 100-to-150-inch zone, has actually 290 inches, and Henderson Lake has had 320 inches in a single year. (For comparison, Regina has 15 inches; Winnipeg, 20; Toronto, 30; Ottawa, 35; Montreal, 42; Halifax, 54.)

As the air sinks down the eastern slopes of the Vancouver Island Mountains, rainfall decreases from over 150 inches to under 100 inches across a zone less than 10 miles wide. In the "rain shadow" of the mountains now, rainfall slackens off to the point where sealevel communities like Victoria and Nanaimo, on the east side of Vancouver Island, are getting 25 to 40 inches. The air moves on across the Strait of Georgia, so water-retaining at this point that rainfall on some of the Gulf Islands drops to under 20 inches a year.

While still out over the strait, the air flow begins to respond to the looming barrier of the mainland's Coast Mountains ahead. Because of air's streamlining tendency, its upper strata begin to rise long before the mountains are reached. Where it first passes over the mainland, rainfall is around 40 inches a year. Thirty miles inland, where it is soaring up the slopes of Garibaldi, it is again dumping out 150 inches per year.

The cluster of weather stations around greater Vancouver sharply illustrate how increasing altitude squeezes more and more water out of air. Vancouver's annual precipitation varies all the way from around 40 inches at the International Airport, 16 feet above sea level, to 130 inches at the meteorological station 2,700 feet up Mount Seymour. Yet these two stations with an annual precipitation difference of 90 inches, three years' rainfall at Toronto, are only 15 miles apart.

The same chaotic precipitation pattern prevails all the way up the coast to Alaska. It is one of the wettest regions of the world, with more than 200 inches in many places. Nevertheless, local variations are extreme, with high land, western slopes and heads of fiords very wet, and low land and western slopes dry, all of which is reflected in the distribution of tree species and forest types. Of course, high altitudes and northern parts of the coast get a greater proportion of their precipitation in the form of snow. Victoria may pass through a winter with no snow at all, whereas Kitimat, at the head of a fiord 400 miles to the north, gets up to 30 feet of snow a winter, and ads are run in the Kitimat newspaper warning children not to step on the hydro wires when climbing roadside snowdrifts.

Precipitation is closely linked with hours of sunshine. Even when it isn't raining, high precipitation areas like the outer coast of Vancouver Island are blanketed for long periods by fog and clouds, reducing evaporation and holding moisture in the soil. In a typical outer-coast December, the sun breaks through the overcast sky for fewer than 10 hours during the whole month, while Victoria is getting 70 hours of sunshine.

The other major ingredient of climate is temperature and its seasonal patterns. In general, the ocean air-conditioner exerts a stabilizing effect, producing mild winters and cool summers, preventing the seasonal extremes that are typical of continental climates inland. The mountains wall off the coast from continental air masses that are cold in winter and hot in summer, so that the coast remains almost permanently under the influence of balmy oceanic air. Only rarely does Arctic air or tropic air spill through the valleys of the Coast Mountains to produce brief winter cold snaps or summer hot spells.

Even the usually consistent effect of latitude on temperature is offset here by the great ocean thermostat which allows only limited temperature variation along the 1,000 miles of coast between Washington and Alaska. In winter, for example, a 50 mile trip inland can take one from 40 degrees on the coast to zero, yet a trip of several hundred miles up the coast will bring a change of only a degree or two.

The west coast is the only part of Canada that has extensive areas with average daily temperatures in the 32°-to-40° range of January means, normally with a few degrees of frost at night and thawing days. Vancouver's usual January temperatures are in the high 30's, Victoria's in the 40's. Victoria experienced its first reading of 0° Fahrenheit in the winter of 1968; the lowest temperature recorded at Victoria was -2 degrees Fahrenheit. Victoria botanists regularly list 25 to 30 species of wild flowers blooming in January, and ornithologists list around 125 species of birds on the Victoria Christmas bird census, the highest for Canada, usually exceeded on the continent by only a few areas in Florida and California. These balmy winters, 22 degrees warmer than is normal for the latitude, are an important element of the coast's invisible ecological cage, for they permit many southern species of plants and trees easily killed by winter frosts, such as arbutus and vine maple, to push slender fingers of range extensions up along the Pacific while remaining absent from the rest of Canada.

Mean daily temperatures for July illustrate the other side of the climate coin—the cool summers. Most of the coast falls within the 55°-to-60° zone of July averages—about the same as Aklavik, 1,200 miles north, above the Arctic Circle. (Comparisons: Winnipeg, 68; Toronto, 71; Montreal, 70.) The Strait of Georgia region, including Vancouver and Victoria, is shielded from direct marine influence by the Vancouver Island Mountains and the Olympic Mountains of Washington and is therefore a little warmer in summer, rising into the 60°-to-65° zone. The heads of major fiords which reach deeply inland also represent small, isolated areas of 60°-to-65° July means; this is because air tends to pocket in such locations and warm up, and also because the hot, continental air of the interior occasionally spills coastward through mountain valleys, warming the fiord heads before the marine air-conditioner can start its cooling work. On the average, fiord heads are about 10 degrees warmer than their mouths in summer.

The growing season, as represented by the average frost-free period, is the longest in Canada. It is greatest in the south and in regions most exposed to the sea, decreasing northward, up the mountains, and also inland up the fiords. The Gulf Islands and the southern tip of Vancouver Island have the longest frost-free period, around 275 days (282 at Victoria). The average date for the last winter frost at Victoria is February 28th, the first frost December 7th. This means that some degree of plant growth can continue for all but the three winter months, a fact reflected in the many southern species that grow in the Victoria and Gulf Islands region.

For most of the coast the frost-free period is between 200 and 250 days. Elsewhere in Canada, frost-free periods are: Calgary, 92 days; Regina, 93; Kapuskasing, 83; Toronto, 165; Halifax, 151.

Victorians, living in the balmiest and driest region of the entire coast, have a saying that sums up the whole climate story. They claim that their region is one of perpetual spring and the only part of the coast which can be said to have a climate at all. According to them, the rest of the coast just has rain.

LIFE ON
THE LAND

The temperate climate, abundant rainfall, and isolation of the Pacific coast produce a unique environment for flora and fauna. Among the luxuriant growth of plant and animal life are many species which occur nowhere else in such northerly latitudes.

Intense competition for living space, light and soil is characteristic of the rain forest.

1

2

3

Douglas Fir   Western   Black   Arbutus   Red Alder
              Red Cedar   Cottonwood

4

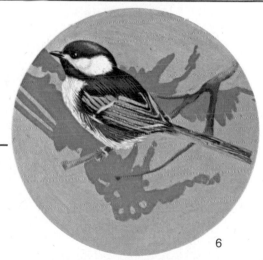

6

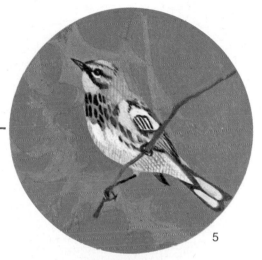

5

7

8

Birds of the forest

Every species of bird has its own niche in the forest habitat which permits it to "earn its living" without competing unduly with other species. Townsend's warbler (1) forages for its insect food high up in the crowns of conifers, often in Douglas firs as indicated in this drawing. It is frequently so high it appears hummingbird-size, but it may nest at a much lower elevation. In contrast, the varied thrush (2) is a forest "basement" bird, feeding low down, often on the ground, in damp, densely shaded underbrush. Rufous hummingbirds (3), are diminutive and brilliant jewels of low-level forest edges and openings where there are flowering plants or trees. The band-tailed pigeon (4) has a habit of perching high up on dead snags or on the tops of cedars, as shown here, but it is a low feeder on elderberry, cascara and dogwood fruits, and often raids grainfields. Audubon's warbler (5) is a bird of high, mountainside, conifer forests and usually descends to lowlands only in winter; sometimes it uses high, exposed perches from which it darts out to catch insects, flycatcher-fashion, in midair. The chestnut-backed chickadee (6) forages for its food at various levels from the mid-stratum to low bushes, in conifers and in deciduous trees like the black cotton wood here; it is also a common town and garden bird. The red-breasted sapsucker (7) drills parallel rows of holes in the trunks of trees, often poplars like this black cottonwood, and then returns later to feed on the sap and insects the sap attracts. The bushtit (8) is a low forager in open deciduous shrubbery like that of the bright-barked arbutus.

A rain-forest nursery

When a fallen log begins to decay, its trunk (below left) becomes a nursery for hundreds of tiny tree seedlings, because the rotting log is a rich source of nutrients and there is no thick mat of moss here as there is on the forest floor. Thirty years later, most of the seedlings have died, but a few (below middle) have sent groping roots down around the log and into the soil below to become sturdy young trees. Slowly, the ancient log rots away from the roots that have splayed around it, taking one to three centuries for the process. Now the trees that began life on the top of the log are left standing on their exposed roots like stilts. In time the roots grow together, filling the space the nurselog once occupied, and giving the trees that grew upon it great, swollen, buttressed bases (below right). The old log has disappeared, but the striking alignment of the trees it nurtured centuries before now resembles a row of trees planted by man, and will remain as long as the trees live to record the nurselog that is gone.

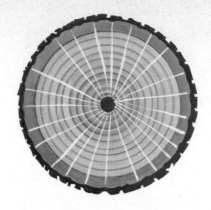

Compressed annual rings at centre of the cross section of a tree (above) record its slow growth before the roots reached soil.

Hundreds of tree seedlings sprout on a fallen log. Decay within the log raises temperature, hastening early growth.

Roots must grow around the nurselog into the soil if saplings are to survive.

The nurselog rots away, leaving the trees that grew on it in an obvious straight row.

Roots spread around old nurselog from swollen base of big tree at right.

Fungus-like Indian pipe is really a parasitic flower.

Abundant bracket fungi often grow as parasites on live trees.

Beautiful rose coral fungus grows where fir-wood debris covers forest floor.

Plant scavengers

Fungi, often brilliantly coloured, are plant scavengers
that play an essential role in
the rain-forest decay cycle
by which the chemicals of life
are returned to the soil for
re-use by other plants. Lacking
chlorophyll which enables
green plants to produce their
own food, fungi have to obtain
their food ready-made. Most of
them do so by living on dead
and decaying organic matter.
A few, however, are parasites
which subsist on living plants
and animals. Both types are
represented in the photographs
on these pages.

Immaculate and delicate oyster mushroom resembles a shell.

Warty skin of baby puffballs will smooth with age.

"Eggs" in tiny bird's nest fungus are spore packets.

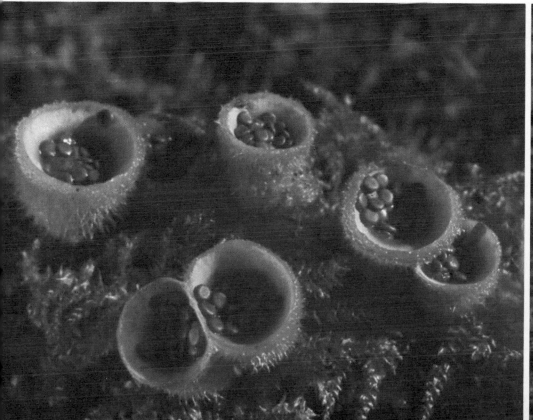

Fly agaric is one of the deadly poisonous Amanitas.

An unusual menagerie

The life of the sea is bizarre and varied, but the Pacific shore's terrestrial life is also a diverse assortment of species. The cougar is a big, tree-climbing, nocturnal hunter, North America's counterpart of the African lion. Its principal prey, the coast deer, has over-sized ears and for this reason is known also as the mule deer. The huge black ears of the long-eared bat are the antennae of its complex "radar" system, by which it localizes ultrasonic echoes of its own voice to guide its flight around obstacles. The little tree frog lives in trees and climbs by means of adhesive disks on its toes.

A tree frog high above the ground.

left: The lithe and power-ful cougar, known also as panther and mountain lion, may weigh 200 pounds.

below: Coast deer, field marks are black tail and two-tined antler forking.

Long-eared bat and relatives are the only mammals that really fly.

A bog story in reverse

The Tofino Bogs represent a complete reversal of normal geological processes. Most bogs start life as relatively shallow lakes which become slowly filled in over a period of years until they eventually become bogs. At Tofino, however, bogs are becoming lakes. The reason is that sands and till deposited by the melting glacier combined with humus and other plant material from the forest to produce a layer of rock-hard sediment which water cannot penetrate. Thus the basin of the land retains all the rain water which does not evaporate and the original bogs get deeper every year and will eventually become small lakes.

The heavily acid soils, intense precipitation, and cool weather combined with the great amounts of humus to produce a "hardpan" of sediment through which water cannot penetrate.

right: As it melts the retreating glacier deposited clay, sand, gravel and till along with vast amounts of water.

far right: The initial forest colonizers, like the Sitka spruce, added their decaying matter to the early soil.

PART THREE / PLANT LIFE

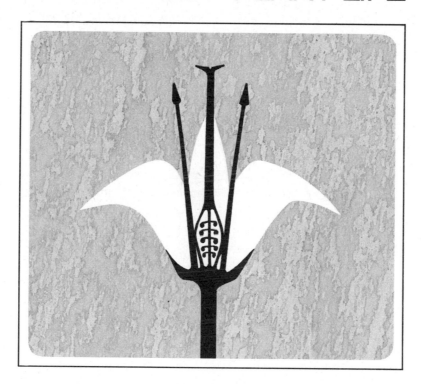

6 FOREST TAPESTRY

Of the many forms of life that make up the Pacific coast's natural history, the most imposing and dominant are its trees.

To the untrained eye, one stretch of forest may not look very different from another. Actually, however, every forest region is a patchwork of many different, interwoven forest types, with one or two tree species dominating it in one spot and other species taking over a little farther on. Such patterns are the result of a complex interacting of many selective factors such as climate, water supply, soil, and the age of the forest itself. A forest is not just a random grab-bag of trees; it has a design, and there is a reason for every tree's being where it is.

Some trees require open sunlight in which to germinate; others require shade. Some need abundant moisture; others have broad water tolerances and can grow on wet or dry sites. Resistance to frost, severe winters, and summer droughts vary widely among different species. Some need a long growing season; some can concentrate the annual growth they need into the brief summers of the Arctic and mountain heights.

No acre of forest is exactly like another in its balancing of all these growth factors. A south-facing slope, for example, will have a different pattern of sunlight, temperature, moisture evaporation, wind exposure, and soil from that of a north slope a few hundred yards away. In the first chapter, we said that the Pacific coast's unique climate created an invisible cage that kept many plant and animal species out, and others in. Within this big cage of the whole coast region, however, lesser variations in climate, soil, and altitude have produced a patchwork of smaller, even less obvious invisible cages which further select and limit the life forms within them.

The most important influence on tree growth in all this is the age of the forest itself, for it is constantly altering its own growth conditions throughout its history. As a forest matures and thickens, the major change is a steady increase in the density of its own shade.

The first generation of trees to colonize bare ground after a fire, wind blow-down, or logging must be species capable of producing seedlings in open sunlight or in the limited shade cast by the first pioneering weeds and bushes. This initial generation of sunlight-demanding species is unable to produce a second generation in its own shade, however, so that the forest growing up under the first trees will have to be different, shade-tolerant species. Eventually, a time is reached when only the most shade-tolerant species are left, that is, trees capable of reproducing themselves perpetually in their own shade, a state of equilibrium that foresters know as the *climax* forest. From now on, as old trees die, there will only be trees of the same species growing up beneath them, and the forest will remain unchanged until another fire, logging, blow-down, or disease epidemic turns back the clock, bares the soil, and starts the process all over again.

This gradual process of change in a forest's dominant species, with increasing shade as its main cause, is called *forest succession.*

In eastern North America, there is a large number of tree species, and as a result, the forests may go through four or five successive stages from pioneer to climax. On the Pacfic coast, however, there are fewer tree species, and the succession story is easier to decipher. Along most of the coast there are only two distinct stages. The pioneering, sun-tolerant species that colonize bare ground to produce the first forest stage are the Douglas fir and Sitka spruce, together with a few other less important, associated species. This initial fir and spruce forest may endure for 1,000 years, but its inevitable fate is to be replaced by the shade-tolerant western hemlock and western red cedar which become the climax. Since all these western trees live longer than trees of the eastern forests, the two-stage coastal succession takes as long to reach its mature climax as does a four- or five-stage one in the east.

Each year every acre of forest land is showered with millions of tree seeds: seeds from the trees already growing there, and seeds carried in by wind and animals from trees in surrounding regions. Only an infinitesimal fraction of these seeds can ever produce trees, and in their silent, hidden, but intense competition for nutrients and growing space, the great invisible sieve of climate, soil, sunlight, and shade is constantly sorting out the seedlings that will survive to someday become the mature forest of the future.

7 THE FOREST CAST

Four trees have starring roles in the Pacific coast's forest cast. They are the Douglas fir, Sitka spruce, western hemlock, and western red cedar.

Douglas fir. This best known of the rain-forest giants is Canada's most valuable lumber producer despite its limited range in Canada as a whole. It is also Canada's largest-growing tree. Mature specimens are commonly six feet in diameter and 200 feet high, but the old giant reaches 14 feet in diameter, more than 300 feet in height, and an age of 1,200 years.

It is a wet-climate tree restricted to the humid, mountainous regions of the west, but it thrives under widely varying conditions, indicating that moisture and climate by themselves set only vague limits to where it can grow. It grows where the annual rainfall reaches 200 inches, but it also does well where rainfall is as low as 30 inches if there is deep soil for over-summer water storage. Climate has little *direct* effect on the distribution of Douglas fir, but in a fascinating, round-about way it does determine in the end where Douglas fir forests will be.

The involved chain of cause and effect starts with the fact that the Douglas fir's most outstanding growth characteristic is the intolerance of its seedlings to shade. A Douglas fir forest requires open or lightly-shaded ground on which to get its start. Once established, it can only be temporary (if an age of 1,000 years can be regarded as temporary!), because no young Douglas firs can grow in the shade cast by their parents. It is replaced in time by the more shade-tolerant hemlock and cedar. Yet the Douglas fir has not disappeared, as this temporary character suggests it should; in fact, pure stands of Douglas fir were probably the most widespread forest type in Oregon, Washington, and southern British Columbia when white men came to the Pacific. The explanation is that fires have been repeatedly levelling parts of the coastal forest, baring the ground to sunlight, and setting the stage for the growth of new Douglas fir forests. Fire and the Douglas fir have been the coast forest's inseparable twins since the Ice Age ended and forest first came back 11,000 years ago.

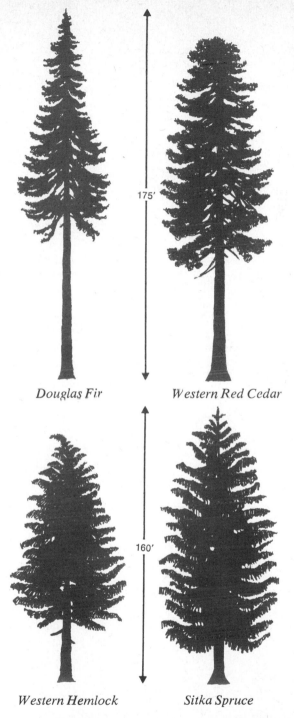

Douglas Fir   Western Red Cedar

Western Hemlock   Sitka Spruce

The most important tree species on the Pacific coast.

Lightning fires during the dry summer months have always been a natural feature of the primeval forest scene. Wherever a pure, even-aged stand of Douglas fir occurs, the presence of charcoal in the soil is telltale evidence that the trees all germinated at the same time following a fire. By removing a boring from one of the trees and counting its growth rings, foresters can determine to within a few years when the fire occurred. On the other hand, a forest of mixed species of uneven age is an old forest that has escaped fire for a long time and is advancing into a later stage of succession. Fires came infrequently to this humid coast, but a severe fire every 500 years would be enough to keep the climax hemlock and cedar suppressed and hold a region permanently in Douglas fir. Thus the distribution of the Douglas fir is closely linked to regions of high fire hazard, and this takes us back to climate, which determines the vulnerability of a region to fire.

The relationship between the Douglas fir and fire-breeding climates can be seen in both small and large scale, in a single mountain valley, and on the Douglas fir distributional map for the whole coast.

In the case of valleys oriented east and west, there is a frequent pattern: Douglas fir forests on the southward-facing slopes where exposure to sunlight has produced summer drying and increased the fire hazard, but older hemlock and cedar forests on the shaded, wetter, northern slopes where the spread of fires has been impeded. Some of the tributaries of the Salmon, Elk, and Englishman rivers on Vancouver Island show a different pattern, with fire-created Douglas fir stands on both slopes, but old, mixed and uneven-aged forests in the wet valley bottoms.

Fire has also shaped the overall distribution of the Douglas fir. In Canada, the gigantic coastal form grows only in the southern 250-mile coastal region approximately to the northern tip of Vancouver Island. It is rare on the wet, outer coast of Vancouver Island and absent from the mainland coast north of the island and from the Queen Charlottes, because rain and fog along these exposed shores and islands have kept forest fires at an almost non-existent level. Inland, however, for another 150 miles north of Vancouver Island to the region of Kemano on Gardner Canal, there are good stands of Douglas fir in many of the sheltered fiord heads, because the fiord heads can have dry, summer hot spells which permit occasional forest fires.

Before logging destroyed the primeval forest pattern, the Douglas fir was the main tree in the dry-summer belt around the Strait of Georgia and throughout most of Vancouver Island, except along its wet, outer coast. Studies by R. L. Schmidt of the British Columbia Forest Research Division show that widespread fires have occurred on Vancouver Island 11 times between 1,200 and 130 years ago. The most extensive of these was about 300 years ago when forests covering approximately a quarter of the island were destroyed. The Douglas fir that sprang up after this gigantic fire was the principal component of the Vancouver Island forest that greeted western man when he first started settling the Pacific Coast.

Sitka spruce. It is the only coastal species of spruce, and *decidedly* coastal, because it grows most commonly right along exposed ocean shores and rarely occurs inland more than 50 miles from saltwater or more than 1,000 feet above sealevel. It is a big tree, but not in the same league with the Douglas fir. The average mature specimen is six feet in diameter and 175 feet high, with the biggest occasionally reaching a diameter of 12 feet and a height of 275 feet.

The Sitka spruce's fondness for the fog belt zone immediately adjacent to the coast has always suggested that this tree derived some essential growth element from open ocean exposures. Dr. V. J. Krajina and a team of students associated with him at the University of British Columbia may have the answer. Through greenhouse experiments using mineral-controlled soils, they found that the Sitka spruce requires much larger amounts of magnesium than do other western trees. Natural soils that are rich in magnesium occur in two situations: in the narrow belt along open coasts where ocean surf is constantly drenching the soil with clouds of salt-saturated spray, and in alluvial, or river-valley soils which are also typically rich in magnesium salts. These two habitats, the ocean-spray zone and alluvial soils, are the situations where Sitka spruce is often the dominant tree.

On coasts, the relationship between the Sitka spruce and ocean spray is sometimes striking. Usually the spruce zone is less than 500 feet wide, but where flat land lets gales carry spray farther inland, the spruce zone will also extend farther inland; and where an island protects a section of coast from surf and spray, the Sitka spruce will be largely absent.

The spruce is apparently a pioneer invader of new ground,

Fireweed provides a beautiful and immediate ground cover in burnt forest areas.

but it is usually associated with wetter soils and climates than fir and is thus less likely to be present in high fire-hazard areas. Windthrow, the uprooting and levelling of forests by gales rather than fire, is what usually gives the Sitka spruce its opportunity to get started. In the ocean-spray zone, living conditions are harsh because of the persistent "saltwater rain," and the Sitka spruce is the only tree that can survive. There it is the climax, because nothing else can move in and replace it. Usually its only woody companion in the ocean-spray zone is the ubiquitous salal, the tough and notorious coast forest shrub that frequently produces an underbrush so dense that a man cannot walk through it.

On ocean exposures the Sitka spruce grows slowly and poorly; on the alluvial soils of inland river valleys it produces trees that rival the other rain-forest giants. But here its fate is that of the Douglas fir–slowly it chokes itself out with its own shade and has to surrender the forest to the more shade-tolerant western hemlock and western red cedar.

Western red cedar and *western hemlock*. They are very different trees, but they are usually associated, and their growth habits and roles in the forest are similar, so they can be considered together.

Western red cedar, unlike the red cedar of eastern Canada

which is little more than a shrub, grows to almost the same great size as Douglas fir and may live even longer.

Western hemlock would be a huge tree in most parts of the world, but here on the Pacific coast it is humbled by the giant cedars and firs with which it grows. It is seldom taller than 150 feet, or more than three or four feet in diameter.

They represent the end of the road in the rain forest's history, for they are the climax species that go on reproducing themselves in their own shade. To get established they require the shade, excessive moisture and water-leached, acid soil that an already existing forest provides. Cedar, hemlock and Douglas fir may all seed down together when a new forest is born on open ground, but the sun-enduring fir will get off to a faster start, over-topping the cedars and hemlocks. Then the shade-tolerant cedars and hemlocks will struggle along as suppressed under-story trees for centuries until the pioneering firs die and the cedars and hemlocks take over the forest by default.

Cedars and hemlocks can survive in shade, putting on little growth, yet remaining alive and ready to burst forth with rapid growth when overtopping trees die and the sun breaks through. In deep forest shade it is not uncommon to find small cedars and hemlocks only a few inches in diameter, yet 200 years old. Most large cedars and hemlocks when logged show this early suppression period vividly in their growth rings—a central core with growth rings packed tightly together when the tree was taking centuries to grow a few inches, then the growth rings suddenly expand from microscopic size to perhaps an eighth of an inch, marking the time when shading trees above died and the stunted sapling could explode with growth.

So cedar and hemlock take over gradually, requiring up to 1,000 years for the process, which means they are usually mixed with species in a forest of uneven age and tree size. Because of the long period they require to get established as the dominant trees, they are more characteristic of wet outer coasts and high-rainfall western slopes where fires rarely occur.

Amabilis fir. Though less abundant than the "big four" described above, it still ranks as an important coastal tree. Usually medium-sized (three feet wide, 125 feet high), it is a slender, symmetrical, beautiful tree with a silver sheen produced by white lines on the lower surfaces of its needles; it is frequently known as lovely fir and silver fir.

Every tree has some critical factor—its Achilles' heel—that sets limits in its fight for a place in the forest. Douglas fir is dependent on fire; Sitka spruce, it seems, has to have the mineral, magnesium; the fortunes of cedar and hemlock are closely linked with density of shade. The weak link in the amabilis fir's ecological chain is an inability to spread its seeds very far. Unlike the seeds of other conifers, amabilis fir seeds are heavy, small-winged, and are carried only limited distances by wind.

Since it is the most shade-tolerant of all the coastal trees, it has a place as a climax species with cedar and hemlock in old forests; nevertheless, it has not exploited this role to the full because of its restricted seed dispersal. Douglas fir is thick-barked, and after a fire there are usually a few of this species left alive to provide seed sources for the reproduction of the burned region. Cedar, hemlock, and amabilis fir are thin-barked, usually destroyed by fire, and have to seed in from surrounding unburned areas. Cedar and hemlock are well equipped to do this, with seeds that travel long distances on the wind, but amabilis fir can invade a burned area only a short distance, then a period of a century or two must pass before this vanguard of invading amabilis firs produces seeds and pushes the invasion a little farther. Thus the amabilis fir migrates in steps, not in one big seed-spreading sweep, and after an extensive fire, 700 to 800 years are required before it has regained a significant place in the forest.

Amabilis fir grows from Oregon to the foot of the Alaskan Panhandle, but it is an important tree only in outer-coast, high-rainfall regions which provide long, fire-free periods. It is entirely absent from the dry inner-coast climatic region around the Strait of Georgia, probably because recurrent fires there have prevented it from gaining a foothold. Its range cuts off abruptly at the southern edge of the Alaskan Panhandle, and the fact that it is a hardy tree which grows in rigorous climatic zones high up mountains is proof that it could also grow much farther north than it does. Why is it not farther north? The answer seems clear. When the Ice Age ended 11,000 years ago, amabilis fir started its creeping march northward up the coast from unglaciated refuges in Washington. For most of the coast's trees, there has been ample time to reoccupy all regions climatically suitable for them, but the amabilis fir, with its slow rate of migration, is apparently still plodding on northward, the colonization that began 11,000 years ago not yet completed. It has extended its range 600 miles in 11,000 years; it has possibly another 600 miles to go before the colder Alaskan climate will finally halt its northward spread. So the amabilis fir's limited range is dramatic proof that life is still in the process of recovering from the long, frigid, smothering death of the Ice Age.

Grand fir. Larger than its close relative, the amabilis, it can produce trees with a diameter of five feet and a height close to 250 feet. It is intolerant of shade and belongs with the Douglas fir as a colonizer of new ground after fires. But it is a warm-climate tree with most of its range southward in the U.S., and on the Canadian coast it occurs only in the dry-warm-summer region around the Strait of Georgia. It is a fairly common species there, but it is much shorter-lived than the other rain-forest giants (old at 300 years), which eliminates it early in the forest history and prevents it from being as common as the Douglas fir with which it usually grows.

On the coast, it is limited to low altitudes, rarely occurring on mountainsides higher than 1,000 feet, and this may be the main factor limiting its spread. There are probably regions outside its present range where it could grow, but it cannot climb mountain to get there. It cannot even migrate up valleys where the valley bottoms exceed 1,000 feet.

Shore pine. This stunted, shrubby, contorted tree grows only on the most exposed, wind-lashed, rocky coasts, sand dunes, and high ridges, or in sodden, highly acid peat bogs—in short, on all the sterile, inhospitable sites where grander trees cannot grow. Inland, the same species is known as lodgepole pine and there it is a sturdy, lumber-producing tree, but the coastal variety is a weak competitor that cannot win and hold a place among the rain-forest stalwarts. It survives only because it is a hardy and adaptive exploiter. It can live a long time, just surviving, putting on little growth. On northern Vancouver Island there are shore pines 370 years old that have grown to trees 18 inches in diameter and 50 feet high, but these are the giants of its breed.

Normally, it is small and grotesque, its knobby limbs twisted by wind; by coast forest standards it hardly ranks as a tree. But there is a good reason for including it in the coast forest story. Though crowded off-stage to the barren sidelines today, it once had a commanding role in the early scenes of the drama when forest was first creeping back behind the receding glaciers. The

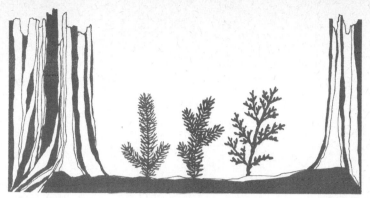

Douglas Fir   Hemlock   Cedar

Fir   Cedar   Hemlock   Fir   Cedar   Fir   Hemlock   Fir

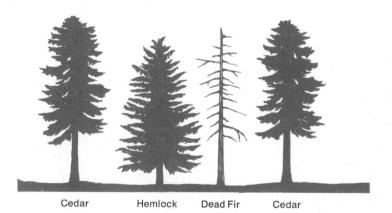

Cedar   Hemlock   Dead Fir   Cedar

Following a major fire all the forest trees begin to grow; Douglas fir soon outstrips the others and prevents them from obtaining needed sunlight. With the death of the fir trees the cedar and hemlock come to dominate the forest.

growing characteristics that have relegated it to the status of a woody weed in the modern forest were once urgently needed by this land. The towering rain forest could not exist today if the scraggy shore pine had not been there to set the stage.

All the foregoing trees have been needle-leafed, cone-bearing trees, popularly known as evergreens. The other major class of tree–the deciduous, broadleafed group that shed their leaves every autumn–is more characteristic of drier climates, but a few have adapted to the wet Pacific region and have carved out modest forest roles.

Red alder and black cottonwood. They are pioneering trees that win their place in the sun by virtue of being rapid growers, which often lets them get established on new ground ahead of Douglas fir. Because of their intolerance to shade and short life spans, however, they soon yield to fir or other conifers. Black cottonwood, one of the poplars, is a thirsty tree that needs wet soil and is usually confined to river bottom-lands. Red alder is frequently the tree that seeds in and heals the wounds of landslides which have swept down coastal mountains. In such circumstances, the red alder is recognizable from offshore as a gray swathe in winter, light green in summer, amidst the dark green of the surrounding conifers.

Broadleaf maple. The only coastal maple that grows to a large tree, it earns its name by bearing leaves a foot wide. It is more shade-tolerant than alder and cottonwood, and often grows as scattered trees in the dark, wet rain forest under firs, cedar, and hemlock. The broadleaf maple is the rain forest's only large deciduous tree.

Garry oak and *arbutus*. This unusual twosome are aberrant "oddballs" in the coast's cast of trees, and have special niches in the coastal forest tapestry. They grow only in British Columbia's southernmost coastal corner where their shaggy, twisted growth form makes them attention-getting trees that contrast sharply with the soaring, rain-forest conifers. Dry-soil and mild-winter trees, they are regarded by foresters as "indicator" species that mark the limits of the Dry-Inner-Coast climatic subregion.

Garry oak, a medium-sized tree on good sites but a gnarled, bushy shrub on rocky ground and exposed coasts where it most frequently grows, is the only species of oak native to British Columbia. It is restricted to southeastern Vancouver Island and the nearby Gulf Islands, with only a few scattered groves on the mainland. A southern tree, it finds only borderline climatic and growth conditions here at the northern extremity of its range. As a result, it reproduces slowly and is a weak competitor against other trees. Once common around Victoria, it is now becoming rare, much to the alarm of the Victoria Natural History Society. Victoria's urban sprawl is engulfing much of its former habitat, and within the city old trees are dying and few

HOW TO IDENTIFY THE TREES

The simplest way to identify any tree is to examine its leaves. The illustration here shows the leaves and outline of some of the more common Pacific coast trees.

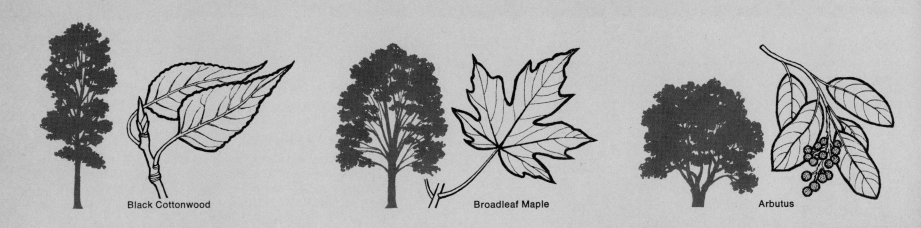

Black Cottonwood

Broadleaf Maple

Arbutus

young ones replacing them because of the species' slow reproduction at this northern latitude.

Arbutus, known also as madrone, is a striking medium-sized tree with twisted limbs and smooth, mottled, reddish bark, vivid in sunlight, that looks like nothing else north of the Mexican tropics. A relative of the tropical rhododendrons and azaleas, it is a broadleafed evergreen that holds its leathery, glossy leaves all winter, another tropical characteristic. It is the only broadleafed evergreen in Canada.

Mountain hemlock, yellow cedar and *alpine fir*. Though usually small trees or sprawling shrubs of the subalpine zone, occasionally one does establish itself at a more hospitable lower altitude, and here it may grow to a sizeable tree. There have been yellow cedars six feet in diameter, 150 feet high, and more than 1,000 years old.

Alpine fir, the picturesque, conical tree of most mountain timberline photos, has a puzzling range on Vancouver Island that has become a subject of dispute between foresters and geologists. It is entirely absent from the southern part of the island, despite the fact that there are many mountain habitats there where it could be growing. Furthermore, in the central part of the island, where the alpine fir is a relatively common high-altitude tree, it grows only on mountains that have an altitude of 4,500 feet or more, and is puzzlingly absent from mountains that do not have peaks reaching that altitude. It is assumed that trees migrated northward from unglaciated areas in the south following the Ice Age, but if the alpine fir followed this route and passed across southern Vancouver Island, why isn't it growing there now?

Foresters contend that the alpine fir's isolation to central-Vancouver-Island mountains with that critical height of 4,500 feet must mean that Ice Age glaciers reached only that height on the island, and that the alpine fir survived the Ice Age on these highest, unglaciated peaks. Since then, the foresters' argument goes, the alpine fir has only been able to spread down the same mountains that provided these ice-free refuges, and no farther. If not, they ask, what other explanation is there for the alpine fir's absence from every mountain with a peak lower than 4,500 feet? But the geologists claim there *has* to be another explanation. They say that all the geological evidence indicates that Vancouver Island was completely ice-covered during the Ice Age, that even its highest 7,000-foot peaks did not protrude above the ice. Hence, the alpine fir puzzle remains.

There are a number of other bit players, but this is the main cast. In the next chapter we will read the record of pollen grains preserved deep in ancient peat bogs for the history of how trees moved in behind the retreating glaciers to produce the forest tapestry of today.

The cones take the place of leaves when identifying the coniferous trees. The cones grow upward on the alpine fir and downward on the mountain hemlock. The needles of the fir and hemlock are also shown to aid identification.

Alpine Fir

Mountain Hemlock

Orange flowers of the tiger lily have rolled-back petals, hang like bells.

Pink Easter lily is rarer than white-flowered species, grows primarily on Vancouver Island.

Coastal Fritillaria lilies have brown flowers, interior species yellow.

Western trillium's white petals turn pink with age. Leaves and flowers are on the same stem, so plant dies when picked.

Tiny bog-growing sundew is an insect-eating plant. Sticky red hairs around each leaf trap insects which are digested for their protein.

Leave them be for others to see

Long summers, mild winters and abundant rainfall produce an incredibly varied coastal flora that changes strikingly from season to season. The annual cycle of this constantly altering carpet of colour is an integral part of the coast's famous scenery. Because of the region's unique climate, many wildflower species found here can grow nowhere else in Canada. The species vary greatly at different mountain altitudes and some of the most beautiful flower communities are in alpine meadows high above timberline, where brief summers and long, severe winters contrast sharply with the benign climate of the coastal lowlands. Many of the region's flowers belong to the lily family, including four of the species shown on these pages. To pick them often kills the plant because leaves have to be picked with the flower, leaving nothing to manufacture food for the underground bulb.

right: Skunk cabbage has its flower spike in a yellow sheath.

8 THE POLLEN RECORD

On the northern outskirts of Victoria, near busy Patricia Bay Highway which leads to the airport and Swartz Bay ferry terminal, there is a low, swampy, pine-grown area known as Rithet's Bog. It is only about 800 feet in diameter, its pines are small, and the ground is a soggy, springy mat of sphagnum moss. It is surrounded now with suburban bungalows, is regarded as an eyesore and mosquito-breeder, and is fated almost certainly to be drained and filled before long as Victoria reaches out for new building space.

In spite of that, however, the 30 feet of peat that underlie Rithet's Bog contain a fascinating record of the region's postglacial history. It is a living museum worthy of preservation, but in an age that regards bogs as obstacles to efficient, urban land-use, only naturalists and a few university scientists are interested in preserving it.

Bogs like Rithet's are depressions in bedrock that fill with water and start their lives as stagnant, land-locked ponds. Sedge and sphagnum moss, the ubiquitous and irrepressible colonizers of wet places, begin growing along the pond's edge and then float out over its surface like a mat. Successive generations of sedge and sphagnum die and are gradually pressed downward by the weight of new growth on the surface, becoming compressed into water-logged peat. Eventually, the pond is choked with peat and other plant debris washed in from the land around until no water remains. Because of the lack of oxygen under the water and a concentration of organic acids, bacterial action is suppressed and the peat is preserved against decay. In time, the peat surface dries enough to let water-tolerant trees move in and clothe it with forest.

The various plant materials composing the peat, though compacted and pulverized, remain identifiable because of the limited decay. One of the best preserved of the peat components are the microscopic pollen grains that rain down annually onto the bog from trees of the surrounding forests. Each tree has its own distinctive, identifiable pollen, so that by taking borings of peat out of a bog and charting the amounts and species of pollen in the various layers that lie in chronological order, the result is a history, not only of the bog, but also of the forests around it. Then, by carbon dating the peat, the whole story can be given a time sequence.

This pollen record has been read from many bogs along the Pacific coast, yielding a detailed story of how forests came back behind the receding ice fronts and of how forests and climate have changed during the 11,000 year postglacial era. Rithet's Bog was studied in this way by David Zirul and Dr. Edwin M. Hagmeier of the University of Victoria.

The story of Rithet's Bog begins as a slightly softer pocket of bedrock under the 4,000 foot-thick tongue of glacier that was flowing out Juan de Fuca Strait. Thousands of years of moving ice gradually rasped out this softer rock to form a basin 30 to 40 feet deep. About 13,000 years ago the fluctuating, outer fringe of the ice sheet shifted back at this point and uncovered the rock basin, but the land was depressed about 250 feet by its ice load, and the area of Rithet's Bog was still ocean bottom. The first page of the bog's story that appears at the base of Zirul and Hagmeier's drill cores is a layer of marine clay deposited over the rock. This clay is well known because it underlies all of the Victoria area, and its texture and the marine shells it contains indicate the type of sea that deposited it. Originally it was open, exposed sea, but at the next level the clay reveals that it had become quieter, protected water. At this stage, the land was lifting above the sea, and Rithet's Bog was now the head of a saltwater bay running southward to the ocean over the site of present-day Victoria.

This condition lasted more than 2,000 years. Then, on top of the marine clay, the first signs of sedge peat begin to appear, indicating that about 10,000 years ago the rising land had cut it off from the sea, and Rithet's Bog had become a cold, freshwater lake, because sedge does not grow in saltwater. Now small amounts of pollen and plant debris begin to show in the peat cores, revealing that the land around was becoming clothed with its first scattered patches of vegetation.

The land surface left by the receding glaciers was sterile. There were mineral sands and gravels; and bare rock in many places, with little humus yet from decaying plant materials. The pollen record shows that the first tree to move back into this inhospitable environment was the tree that still grows in such harsh, unwanted sites today, the shore pine. It was ideally suited for this first essential "taming" job on the glacier-scoured land. It could grow almost any place – on dry sand, in cracks of rocks, on the vast, sodden, alluvial mudflats fanning out in front of the glaciers. Since it starts producing seed as early as its sixth year, it was able to keep pace with the retreating ice, probably growing right up against the fissured, shattering ice fronts. In fact, where stagnant masses of ice became covered with layers of mud, shore pine probably grew *on* the ice itself, as it does in places in Alaska today, not even waiting for the ice to disappear.

We can be sure that this first covering of pine hardly rated being described as a forest. Its trees were dwarfed and crooked, fighting inclement weather and sterile soil to stay alive, yet it must have been abundant, because in Rithet's and all other bogs studied, a mixture of sedge peat and pine pollen forms the major preserved layers directly on top of the lowermost rock, clay or gravel of the bog foundations. There is little record of other trees at these lowest levels. During this first postglacial interval, shore pine had the land virtually to itself, creating a scraggly green sea so near the ice that it appeared to be pushing the ice before it, rather than following in its wake. A despised "weed" tree today, it was the "right man for the right job" then, anchoring the newly formed land, producing humus, providing shelter for other plants and trees to follow.

Much of the glacial till that forms the foundation for thousands of square miles of coastal forest lands today would have been scoured away by rushing meltwaters and carried into the Pacific were it not for the prompt colonizing of this redoubtable forest pioneer. If a grateful forest industry wants to start raising monuments to its important trees, the first one should not be for the celebrated Douglas fir, but for the stunted, deformed, persistent shore pine.

The shore pine was short-lived, however, and intolerant of its own shade. It could pioneer new land, but not retain it. Perhaps its heyday lasted 1,000 years while the shifting of melt streams, the breaking out of ice-dammed lakes, and the deposition of new mud strata kept the land too unstable for longer-lived trees to get established. But as soon as the land attained some permanency, new invaders came to claim the terrain that the shore pine had tamed.

The pollen record varies somewhat from bog to bog, depending on local topography and exposure to the sea, so that

LAYERS OF A BOG

The highly acidic character of certain Pacific coast bogs has caused them to preserve pollen from ancient trees in an almost perfect condition. A drill core passed down through these bogs thus reveals the pollen from the trees which grew on the land when the various layers of the bog were exposed to the surface. The illustration at right shows the various trees which flourished in the area of the bog during the last 10,000 years.

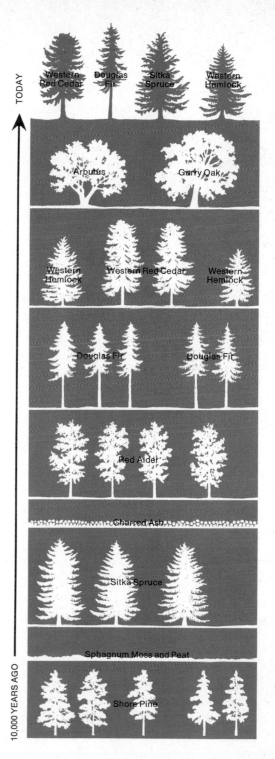

75

no single bog tells the postglacial forest history for the whole region. In order to form a general picture for the region, it is necessary to combine the main features of pollen records from numerous British Columbia and Washington State bogs.

Soon after the pine was established, sphagnum moss joined the sedge in most bogs as a major component of the peat, indicating an increasing acidity and a switch from pond-edge marsh to true bog. The rate of peat accumulation now accelerated to three to four inches per century, a rate that continues to the present time.

For bogs like Rithet's near the sea, the next tree pollen that begins to appear with that of shore pine is that of the Sitka spruce, adhering to the coastal strip then as it does today. Elsewhere in southern British Columbia, the second tree to grow up in the thin shade of the pines was the Douglas fir, the tree that is the main colonizer of new ground at the present time. The pollen record shows that the pine now disappeared. The time was 9,000 to 8,000 years ago along the southern coast, a thousand years or so later farther north, where the ice lingered longer.

Some bog borings show charred particles indicating that fire was a forest destroyer. Often, immediately above a charred layer, there is a sudden and tremendous increase in pollen of the red alder, showing that this deciduous, fast-growing pioneer sometimes sneaked in following a fire to produce a single generation of broadleafed forest before the Douglas fir could fight its way back.

By 8,000 years ago another pollen had appeared, portending forest changes. It is that of the western hemlock, the shade-tolerant climax species of older forests, and its appearance means that the soil was now growing richer from the slow build-up of humus and the work of soil-maturing fungi and bacteria. Fluctuations of western hemlock and Douglas fir pollen in the peat profiles dovetail neatly; where hemlock increases, Douglas fir declines, and vice versa, recording how fires aided the spread of Douglas fir, and how periods without fires let the hemlock creep back, ousting the fir. There is one gap in the pollen record, however, for cedar pollen does not preserve in acid peat as all others do, and it is conspicuously absent from all these lower peat borings. Foresters assume that wherever western hemlock appears in the pollen profiles, western red cedar was also there, for the two trees are usually associated today.

Some 8,000 years ago, the pollen records show a dramatic and sudden change. All around the northern world at this time, southern plants and trees began extending their ranges northward, because the climate suddenly turned drier and warmer. This period, known as the *xerothermic period,* lasted for the next 4,000 years. Its cause is still not understood, but it was so widespread and longlasting that most authorities feel it must have resulted from an increase in radiation from the sun itself.

Along the Pacific, the xerothermic period was not as pronounced as elsewhere, because of the weather-stabilizing influence of the sea, but even here it brought major adjustments in vegetation. Pollens of the moisture-loving Sitka spruce and hemlock almost disappear, pollens of southern species moved into the Strait of Georgia region begin to show up, establishing range expansions that they have been able to hold through subsequent cooler and wetter climates to the present day.

As one moves up the peat cores into levels deposited 4,000 years ago, the pollen ratios change again. Hemlock and Sitka spruce, the moisture-demanding trees, gradually become better represented; the dry-climate Garry oak and arbutus become scarcer. The dry-warm xerothermic period had ended. The climate, wetter and a little cooler, had returned to what it was some 4,000 years before, and the hemlock and spruce were moving back southward now from northern regions where the xerothermic interval had driven them.

The pollen records reveal that about this time the forest assumed the species composition it has today—Sitka spruce a dominant in the north, and southward along the coastal fringe; cedar and hemlock winning dominance in wet, fire-free regions; and Douglas fir assuming the commanding role wherever drier climate permitted periodic fires. For the last 4,000 years this remained the pattern until recent logging by man brought drastic change again.

But there is one more interesting and ironic change in the pollen profiles of the bogs themselves. During the last thousand years or so, in many bogs, including Rithet's, the peat becomes dominated again by a familiar pollen that had been virtually absent since the earliest postglacial period. By this time many bogs had become so filled with peat that the peat itself became capable of supporting tree growth. But soggy and highly acid, peat is a sterile and inhospitable growth medium for trees. Only one tree will grow on it, the tree the bogs knew well in an earlier and harsher time – our old friend, the irrepressible shore pine. So the pollen record comes back full circle to its starting point. Once more it is packed with the pollen of shore pine, this time not from stunted pine forests reclothing a denuded, glacier-ravaged landscape, but from pines that have returned to invade the bogs themselves. Again the pine is pioneering, because where conditions are right the pine may build up the bog surface, induce better drainage and create a drier site into which other trees can move. Then the pine once more will surrender and disappear, and the bog will disappear with it; only the ancient peat record hidden deep below will remain.

9 RAIN FOREST

"Rain forest" is not a scientific term; it is simply a popular name for old forests in the wet Pacific coastal belt where superabundant moisture has permitted the development of huge long-lived trees. The name has come to mean forests that have the following elements – big trees in dense stands, a pervading wetness, and a lush associated growth of moisture-demanding mosses and ferns that often grow high up the trees themselves.

In most parts of the world, a tree is tall at 100 feet. Big trees in the tropic rain forests go to 175 feet. But in mature Pacific rain forests, the trees *average* 200 feet and the giants are over 300.

There are two reasons for the great height of Pacific coast trees. In every forest the trees are in vigorous competition to lift their leaves up into sunlight where the most efficient food production takes place. The raw materials from which trees manufacture the cellulose that goes into wood production are carbon dioxide, taken in by leaves from the air, and salts and water from the soil. The limiting factor to growth is usually the amount of water available to transport salts from the roots to the leaves. The abundance of water provided by the Pacific coast climate and the long growing season ensure that tree growth continues with a minimum of interruption. The second reason is that conifers are a long-lived group, the Pacific coast conifers strikingly so. Growth of a tree slows down with age, but never comes

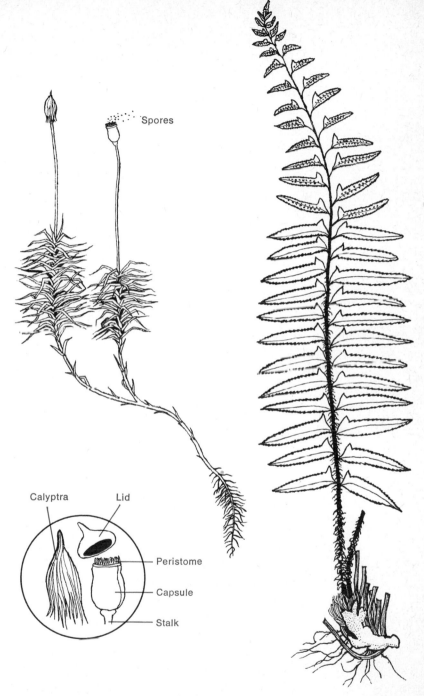

The true mosses (left) have changed little in 300 million years. Spores are released from vase-like structures. The sword fern's roots (right) are an emergency source of food.

The virgin forests of the Pacific coast produced many trees so huge their stumps could be used as a dance floor.

to a full stop. So the combination of long-lived trees and super-abundant moisture pushes the race for sunlight to heights impossible in other forests.

Mature, huge treed rain forest didn't cover all the coastal region originally, by any means. It didn't extend up mountainsides very far and was rare on rain-shadowed, eastern mountain slopes. Its development required at least a couple of centuries without fire, so it was sparsely distributed in the dry-summer, inner-coast region and at the mainland fiord heads. Nevertheless, it *was* widespread, especially in the wet lowlands near the sea. But its tendency to concentrate in lowlands and coastal areas held the seeds of its destruction, for it put the most commercially valuable stands where they were readily accessible to loggers. As a result, practically all the primeval rain forest is gone today except from a few parks and reserves, and in out-of-the-way valleys that loggers have not yet reached.

There are examples of big trees in Vancouver's Stanley Park, and in Goldstream and other parks near Victoria. Goldstream has a few splendid 500-year-old cedars. But these are isolated trees, just sample copies, no longer in their full and genuine rain-forest setting.

The best example of readily accessible virgin rain forest north of the redwood and sequoia groves in California (which are rain forests of a different type) is in Washington State's Olympic National Park across the Strait of Juan de Fuca from Victoria. But several parks on Vancouver Island, such as Miracle Beach, Wickaninnish Beach, Elk Falls and big 830-square-mile Strathcona, have good virgin or near-virgin rain-forest stands. However, the best one, the jewel of British Columbia's rain forest preserves, is Cathedral Grove, 20 miles west of Parksville. It is possible to drive right into it, because the Alberni highway that crosses the island from Parksville to the outer coast at Tofino cuts like a narrow gorge directly through Cathedral Grove's tallest Douglas firs. It is one of the most impressive remnants of virgin Canada that we have; it deserves to be as well known as Niagara Falls.

One is drawn with humility and awe into the nature trail that circles for a quarter of a mile among Cathedral Grove's great trees. Most of the biggest trees are Douglas fir, with some grand fir and a few red cedars, and the appropriateness of the Grove's name strikes one at once, for the trunks rise straight and true like fluted cathedral columns to a green arch of interlocking branches 200 feet above. The forest interior is an eerie gloom with a greenish hue from light filtering through the latticework of needles and from the vivid reflected greens of sword ferns and mosses that clothe the forest floor. Occasionally the gloom is lanced by a slanting shaft of sunlight where a limb above has died or fallen and left a wound in the canopy not yet healed by new growth. The wetness that produces it all is obvious everywhere–small tendrils of fog play through the upper branches even on clear days, water drips constantly, and the thick moss cushions on the ground squish like sodden sponges when trod upon.

Cathedral Grove has two main age classes of trees–800-year-olds and 300-year-olds. The 800-year-olds survived a fire that partially opened the forest 300 years ago, letting a scattered new generation of Douglas firs get established at that time.

The tallest measured tree is 275 feet high, the equivalent of a 23-story building; the tree of greatest diameter is nine-and-a-half feet through and contains enough lumber to build three frame houses. As you gaze at this dynasty of giants, ponder the startling fact that each one, weighing several hundred tons today, started life as an almost invisible seed so small that it takes 2,500 of them to weigh an ounce. The 275-footer, incidentally, may not be the tallest, for in all rain forests the tops of trees are always obscured by the forest canopy, and height measurements using sighting instruments from the ground are difficult. Height records are constantly being broken all along the coast as new, taller trees are discovered.

Because of its dense shade, Cathedral Grove, like all intact rain forests, is surprisingly open underneath. There are no young Douglas fir; the only young trees in the understory are shade-tolerant western hemlock, a preview of what Cathedral Grove will be centuries from now when its fir trees die out. Ground cover, except for the thick carpet of mosses and lichens, is scant and restricted to a few shade-tolerant species, mainly sword-fern, but also vanilla leaf, trillium, silver-green and wall lettuce. Rain forests are not good hunting grounds for botanists. Nor are they for birdwatchers, because the deep shade produces little seed or insect food for birds. The rain forest floor usually has a few winter wrens, and the canopy high above may have woodpeckers, nuthatches, brown creepers, golden-crowned

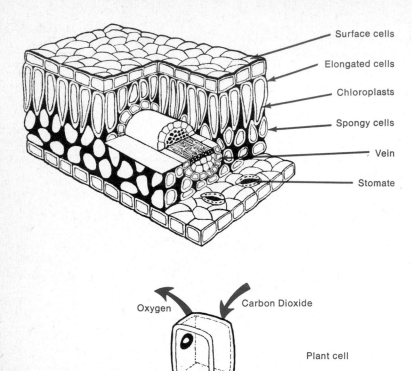

Surface cells

Elongated cells

Chloroplasts

Spongy cells

Vein

Stomate

Oxygen

Carbon Dioxide

Plant cell

Food

Water

This magnified cross-section of a leaf clearly shows the cellular structure. Sunlight passes through the outer protective cells and enters the elongated cells which contain most of the chloroplasts used in the manufacturing of food. The stomates in the elongated cells on the underside of the leaf provide an entrance for carbon dioxide. The veins provide an entrance for water and other nutrients which the leaf needs. Water vapour and oxygen are released to the air through stomates while the veins carry food to all parts of the tree.

kinglets, western flycatchers and chestnut-backed chickadees, but, in general, birds prefer more open forest or forest edges and avoid the damp, gloomy aisles of the rain forest's interior.

Almost as impressive as the massive trees are the lush hanging gardens of ferns, mosses and lichens that drape tree trunks and limbs in a shaggy upholstery almost to their tops. These are what botanists call *epiphytes*–plants that use another plant for support but are not parasites. All they seek from the trees to which they cling is a platform nearer the sun. Their main requirement is water and there is no lack of it in their humid treetop world; for soil they can make do with the few particles of atmospheric dust, pollen and wind-borne plant debris that lodge in the bark crannies. It is an uncanny experience for a naturalist visiting a rain forest for the first time to raise his binoculars and identify the slender, drooping fronds of a polypody fern growing on a trunk 150 feet up in the air. And there are some 90 other species of epiphytes that grow on rain-forest trees.

West of Cathedral Grove on the outer coast around Tofino there is so much moisture that epiphytic mosses and lichens grow in beardlike tassels even from roadside telephone wires.

A sharp observer will be struck by another rain-forest oddity–in places he will see trees with swollen, buttressed bases strikingly lined up in rows as though they were planted by man. They record an interesting story in a battle for growth that occurred centuries ago–the story of the nurselog.

When a tree crashes to the ground the decay of its log under rain-forest conditions is very slow; size alone is one of the reasons for this, and another is that excessive moisture so saturates the log that there is little space for the oxygen which decay-producing fungi need for their growth. Downed spruce and hemlock logs require a century to rot, Douglas fir and red cedar three times as long. The thick carpet of moss on the forest floor makes it difficult for tree seeds to germinate and survive long enough to push their roots through to the underlying humus and soil, but when decay has started on a downed log its top becomes an excellent nursery for small trees. There is less competition with mosses there, and the decay process going on within the log increases temperature and makes chemicals more available, so before long there are usually several young trees growing along the length of every prostrate log.

But the young trees cannot survive indefinitely on their

nurselog habitat; eventually they must get their roots down into the soil. So some of the roots reach out and downward around the outside of the log, sometimes taking 50 years before their groping growth finally reaches soil six or eight feet below. Eventually the nurselog rots away from around the roots of the trees it nurtured and the trees are left standing on splayed roots like stilts. In time the roots grow together, filling the space that the rotting log had occupied, producing the swollen, buttressed bases. Then for centuries afterwards the trees will keep growing, their striking alignment the only record left of the nurselog that belonged to an earlier generation of forest and gave them birth.

10 PATRIARCHS AND GIANTS

Although Cathedral Grove is the finest, most easily visited rain forest, it has neither the biggest nor the oldest single trees. Where are the record-setting monarchs, past and present? How do they compare with tree giants in other parts of the world?

In the old days, when lumbering was an uncontrolled scramble to get the biggest trees before someone else did, records of tree dimensions were not always kept. The largest trees went first, and it is possible, if not probable, that trees cut then and unrecorded were bigger than anything known today.

The world's largest trees are two Pacific rain forest species that do not grow as far north as Canada: the coast redwood of the northern California coast, and the giant sequoia of the wet Sierra Nevada slopes in the California interior.

The tallest known tree on earth today is a coast redwood 385 feet high found in June, 1966, in Redwood Creek Valley of northern California. It is 17 feet in diameter.

Tallest trees don't always have the greatest girth, and the tree with the greatest diameter in the world is California's famous General Grant sequoia. It is more than 40 feet across at its base, four times that of the largest Douglas fir in Cathedral Grove!

The Douglas fir is the world's third largest tree, exceeded only by the redwoods and sequoias. In fact, there is an old argument that the biggest tree of all time *was* a Douglas fir, the controversial and legendary "Carey fir" that is said to have been

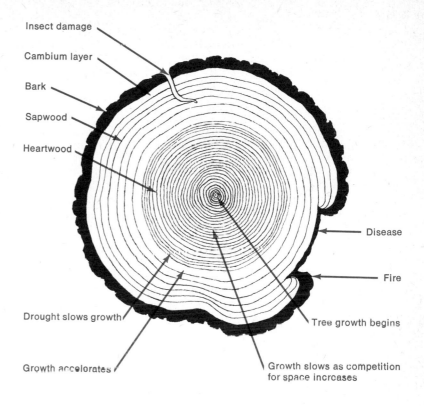

Insect damage
Cambium layer
Bark
Sapwood
Heartwood
Disease
Fire
Drought slows growth
Tree growth begins
Growth accelerates
Growth slows as competition for space increases

Each year a thin layer of cells called the cambium layer adds another growth ring to the tree as it increases in diameter. If these annual rings are counted from the centre you can get a very accurate idea of the tree's age. The width of each ring depends on such factors as the availability of sun, rain, and good soil, competition with other trees for growing space, as well as fire, drought or insect damage. The cross-section of a tree thus provides a picture of its entire life history.

cut in the 1890's by George Carey in Lynn Valley, now North Vancouver. This tree was widely discussed and reported in the 1920's, and there are detailed measurements on record for it. It was said to have been 417 feet high, 300 feet to the first limb, 25 feet in diameter, and still nine feet in diameter at a height of 207 feet. But Carey himself is said to have denied it in later years. Although it is listed at the top of "big tree" records in literature around the world, most modern foresters doubt that there was such a tree. Historians, on the other hand, schooled at assessing the validity of written records and uninfluenced by preconceived ideas about the limits of tree growth, have said that records of the Carey fir from various sources are so consistent in their detail that the tree cannot be discredited just because it seems too big to be believed. As for Carey's own denial, they say it may only indicate that some incredulous foresters succeeded in persuading Carey in his old age that he must have been mistaken. So the Carey fir is still debated, and it will never be known whether it really existed. If there was a 417-foot Douglas fir in North Vancouver's Lynn Valley, it was the tallest living thing ever recorded for all the earth's history.

Verified Douglas fir records come a great deal smaller. The tallest standing today is believed to be one that is 324 feet high at Ryderwood, Washington. British Columbia's tallest Douglas fir is a 305-footer in a roadless and virtually inaccessible region on the Puntledge River in the southeastern corner of Vancouver Island's Strathcona Park. Prior to its discovery in 1964, the biggest verified British Columbia Douglas fir was another 305-footer cut several years ago at Woss Lake on Vancouver Island, a strapping youngster only 385 years old.

The greatest diameter on record for a Douglas fir is 21 feet, possessed by a gnarled giant that grew at Westholme, southern Vancouver Island, and fell as a result of butt-rot on November 29, 1913. Nearby residents thought it was an earthquake. Its age, based on a partial count and estimate of growth rings, was put at 1,500 years, which, if accurate, means that it started growth about the time the Goths sacked Rome and brought the Roman Empire to its knees.

The next greatest recorded diameter was a Douglas fir 14 feet four inches through that was felled in 1886 at the corner of Granville and Georgia streets, now downtown Vancouver.

The occasional western red cedar can match the biggest Douglas firs in diameter but not in height. A cedar that stood at Lonsdale Avenue and Keith Road, North Vancouver, in the 1890's, was 20 feet in diameter at ground level. Others up to 16 feet are on record for the Comox Lake area on Vancouver Island. But maximum cedar heights are around 230 feet. A giant cedar log on display at the Forest Museum near Duncan (an excellent place, incidentally, to absorb the romance of B.C. trees and its forest industry) is eleven-and-a-half feet in diameter, 1,300 years old, but when cut in 1959 was only 156 feet high. Its growth rings reveal that it grew almost twenty inches in its first century but only two inches in its last.

Elsewhere in the world, the closest known runners-up to the Pacific coast's redwoods, sequoias, and Douglas firs are the eucalyptuses of Australia. There is a 322-foot eucalyptus in Tasmania, and a 305-footer in Victoria, Australia. Calcutta's famous banyan treet is 42 feet in diameter, about the same as California's General Grant sequoia, but the banyan is a squat tree, mostly trunk, with little height to complement its gargantuan girth.

In terms of age, Canada's oldest trees are far behind some of California's venerable patriarchs. The oldest living things on earth are bristlecone pines, stunted and shaggy shrubs of the southwestern mountains, specimens of which are known to be 4,600 years old and still living, having sprouted about the time the Egyptian pyramids were being built. The General Grant sequoia is 3,500 years old, and there are redwoods known to be 2,200 years of age. The oldest Canadian tree would be the 1,500-year-old Douglas fir that fell in 1913 at Westholme, but the records say that its age was based on "a partial count and estimate" of growth rings, so that there could be some error. There are also 1,500-year estimates for western red cedars at Seymour Inlet on the mainland near the northern end of Vancouver Island. But the greatest ages based on actual ring counts are 1,320 years for a cedar cut in 1956 on Waterloo Mountain, southern Vancouver Island, and 1,266 years for a Douglas fir cut in 1959 at Cowichan Lake in the same vicinity.

But taking a boring out of a 10-foot tree and meticulously counting 1,000 or more tiny growth rings is a tedious task, and understandingly it has not been widely done. Foresters do not deny that there might be older trees, and bigger ones, too, still standing and growing, awaiting discovery.

SEA-LIFE

The life in the sea forms a dramatic and unique chapter in the Natural History of the Pacific coast. The tidal zone, that area of shoreline which is alternately covered and exposed by the tide, provides a rich mixture of land and sea life. The shallow water sea life remains always close enough to be observed but never loses its "other world" character. The many freshwater streams and lakes on the coast add yet another dimension to the fascinating world of aquatic life.

Salmon often jump high water-falls and overcome other obstacles in an heroic attempt to return to the stream of their birth to mate.

To the sea and back

A pair of sockeye salmon seek a suitable place to spawn. When the female has found the right gravel bed, she will excavate a hollow with her tail and then lay as many as 8,000 eggs. The eggs must have a constant water flow and suitable temperature, but must also be protected from direct sunlight. The newly hatched fish, alevins, have huge eyes and sac-like appendages which contain a completely balanced diet. The vitelline vein, running through the centre of the sac, picks up oxygen from the water. Once they lose the sac, the young salmon are called fry and feed on plankton and small insects. After a year spent in fresh water the fry, now three to four inches long and known as fingerlings, head downstream, sometime before the ice has melted, and enter the open sea. After several years at sea the mature salmon return to the streams of their birth to mate and die. During this period they live off stored body fats. The male develops a humped back and ragged fins, but the female maintains her sleek form.

The male salmon fertilizes the eggs with a milky secretion. They are then covered by gravel, and the female watches over them until she dies.

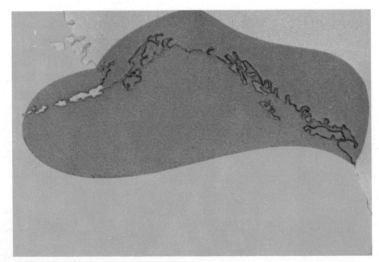

The map above shows the area of the Pacific Ocean in which the salmon live and the spawning rivers along the coast.

Free-swimming, and easy prey now for larger fish, sockeye fry stay upstream about a year before they face the perils of the open sea.

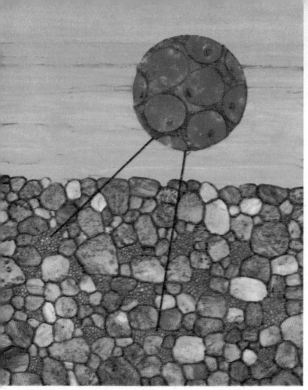

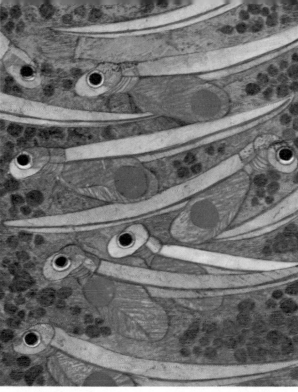

The eggs are deposited in November. About a month later the eyes begin to appear.

In February eggs hatch into alevins which grow rapidly under gravel for the next four months.

In May or June, the alevins emerge as one inch fry.

Salmon spend up to five years eating greedily and growing rapidly. During this period they develop sexually and grow to about 12 pounds.

Salmon eventually return to their birthplace. As they enter fresh water, their silvery blue scales turn crimson.

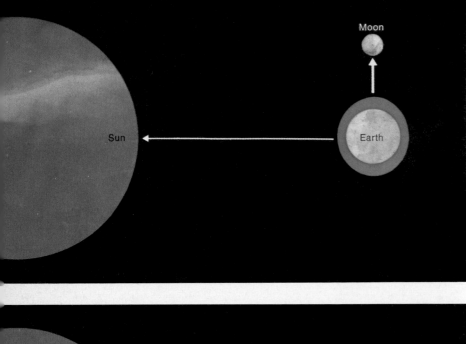

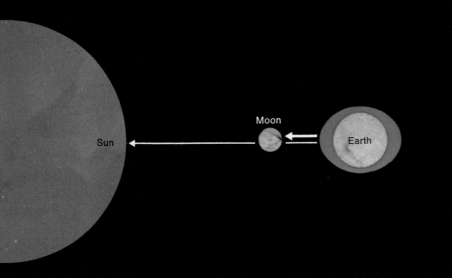

Neap and Spring Tides

Seasonal Current Variations

Cosmic forces create the intertidal zone

Tides are caused by the gravitational pull of the moon and, to a lesser degree, the sun whose combined forces result in huge swells of water forming on both sides of the earth. As the earth rotates beneath the ocean swells, the water level along the coast line alternately rises and falls — a cycle that is repeated twice daily in most areas. When the sun and the moon twice a month lie at right angles to each other (top left), the sun counterbalances and radically reduces the moon's force, to produce comparatively small or "neap" tides. When the sun and moon lie in a direct path with the earth, (bottom left) again twice a month, their combined gravitational force produces exaggerated or "spring" tides.

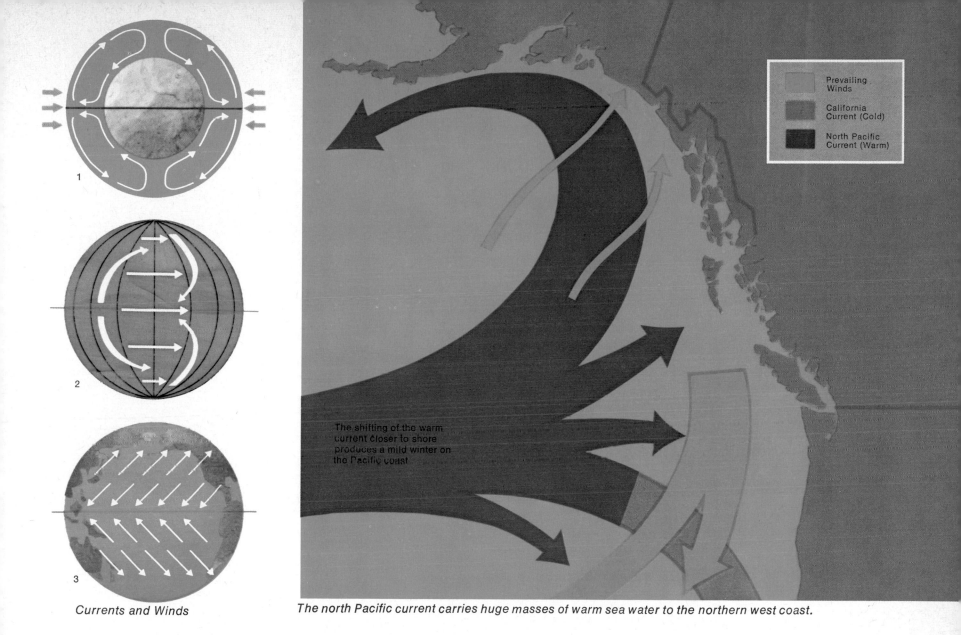

The shifting of the warm
current closer to shore
produces a mild winter on
the Pacific coast

Currents and Winds

The north Pacific current carries huge masses of warm sea water to the northern west coast.

Because of the way the earth rotates, equatorial waters receive the direct rays of the sun and are the warmest. The heat of the surface water around the equator causes it to expand and travel downhill towards the North and South Poles (1). The colder and heavier waters act in reverse, sinking below the warm water and spreading slowly along the bottom towards the equator. As the earth spins more than 1,000 miles per hour at the equator, it tends to spin away from the water (2). The eastward spin results in larger tides forming along western shores. The earth's spin also has a deflecting effect on the winds, causing them to turn slightly to the right in the northern hemisphere, slightly to the left in the southern. This is known as the "Coriolis effect." Wind belts, affected by the nature of the earth's spin drive seas from the east in the tropics and from the west in the higher latitudes (3).

The rich and crowded intertidal zone

left: The various zones of intertidal life are clearly illustrated on the face of this rock at low tide.

A purple seastar forces open the shell of a mussel, then inserts its stomach inside the shell and digests the mussel within.

The intertidal zone is that part of the coastline extending from the lowest level uncovered by tides up to the point washed or splashed by waves at the highest tides. It is a zone astonishingly rich in both numbers and species of animals. The seashore is essentially an extension of the seas, and the animals and plants that live there are almost all of direct marine origin. Most of their activities are reduced when they are temporarily exposed to the air between tides and are resumed in full only when they are once more covered by the returning sea, which is their essential medium for photosynthesis, feeding and breeding.

Ghost shrimp in sand burrow.   Leather chiton, a primitive rock-clinging snail.   The big moon-snail is a beach tunneller.

Vivid pink anemone is an animal, not a flower.   Goose barnacle on drifting log.   Soft coral is an isopod's brilliant home.

The rich and brilliant world between land and sea

The ebb and flow of tides renew twice daily the rich
and bountiful food supply of the intertidal zone.
At its lowest level the zone is covered most of the
time by nourishing seawater, at upper levels it is
covered only briefly each day by the highest tides.
It may be exposed to the hammering surf of the sea,
or found in a protected cove that waves never reach.
Its substratum may be rock, boulders, mud or sand.
Each of these conditions demands a different way
of life and nature has met the profusion of intertidal challenges and opportunities by filling it with
a teeming community of weird, brilliant, fantastic-
ally varied life forms. No other habitat on earth
has such an abundance of contrasting species
sharing so limited an area. It has swimmers, drifters,
crawlers, burrowers. It has its agile hunters — and
benign sitters that spend their lives cemented
to rocks or wharf piles, trusting the restless
pulsing of the sea to bring them food. The pictures
on these pages are a small cross-section of many
hundreds of diverse and colourful seashore species.

*left: The coast garter snake, a swift swimmer, often
catches fish stranded in rock pools by the receding tide. This one is swallowing a clingfish.*

*right: Many umbrella-like jellyfish (above and below)
live in Pacific waters. Long stinging tentacles
stun their prey. Swimmers should avoid them.*

A lingcod finds a small flounder a tasty meal.

Weird world of the undersea

The abundant life of the sea makes the warm waters of the Pacific coast a naturalist's paradise. The richness of sea life is suggested by the few species illustrated here. As everywhere in nature, life is a fierce struggle for food; most bodily characteristics are adaptations made in the long evolutionary struggle for survival.

The male wolf-eel is a formidable sight.

right: A black-clawed crab scurries backward across the bottom.

Rockfish are common along the coast.

The sculpin's natural camouflage makes it almost impossible to see.

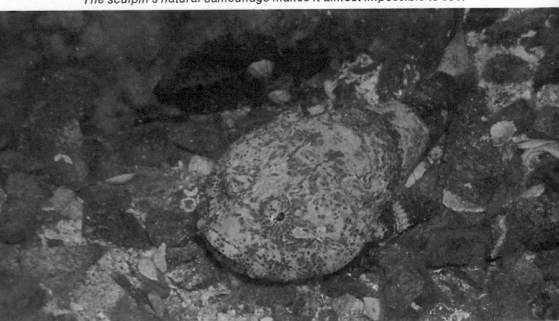

Stellar's sea lions, once plentiful, have become scarce.

PART FOUR / ANIMAL LIFE

11 PASTURES OF THE SEA

There are hazy zones in the tangled classification of living things where plant and animal species merge and it is difficult to say with certainty where plant life ends and animal life begins. One of these zones is the green plankton pastures of the sea, a living world which, though microscopic and little known, is more important in the overall skein of life, greater in aggregate bulk, and more varied in species than the plant and animal empire of the land.

Plankton is the biologist's term for the teeming clouds of minute plants, near-plants, and animals that fill every square foot of seawater, even at tremendous depths. Most of them are plants, or at least more plant-like than animal-like (for example, the hosts of one-celled or few-celled algae) but included under the same plankton label are hordes of tiny animals too. They represent the stage of life at which the simplest plants and animals branched off to follow their different evolutionary paths, and since some of them have attributes of both plants and animals, there is a debate as to which kingdom of life they belong, or whether they should have a separate kingdom of their own.

Most of the sea's plankton are microscopic in size, with the largest barely visible to the naked eye, but in mass they frequently appear as a clouding in the water or as a thin film on its surface.

Seawater is actually a thin soup of this living material. One quart of it may contain 50 million of them, and include 3,000 different species! Though invisible, or nearly so, they represent in total volume what is far and away the greatest mass of life on earth, for they are spread throughout the earth's biggest life-supporting zone. In terms of surface alone, there is twice as much ocean as land, but in addition to this the oceans have an average depth of more than two miles, most of which teems with plankton life, whereas terrestial life can occupy only a thin film of land and air a few hundred feet in depth. No matter how you want to look at it—in aggregate bulk, number of individuals, or number of species—the plankton of the sea form the greatest of all living worlds.

There are good reasons why the plant or plant-resembling members of the plankton differ so strikingly from plants of the land.

The sea is the richest domain of life in nature because seawater is a nearly perfect medium for building and maintaining protoplasm, the basic structural material of all living organisms. It is a much more bountiful provider of nutrients than air and soil. On land or sea, the essential ingredients of life and growth are water, carbon dioxide, mineral salts, and oxygen. Land plants have to work hard to obtain these basic life ingredients, establishing complex root systems and constantly lifting water and salts up into leaves where they are combined with carbon dioxide to produce plant carbohydrates. But in the sea, plants are permanently immersed in a readymade solution containing all these life-supporting nutrients. The supply is unlimited; all

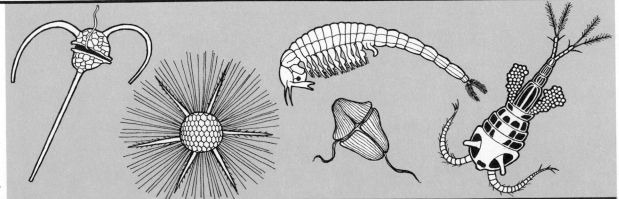

All natural, unpolluted fresh and salt water is a thin, living soup of microscopic plants and animals, a few are shown in these enlarged drawings. They are known as plankton. There are thousands of species and a quart of seawater may contain millions of individuals. They are the basic food of the sea, the foundation on which every marine food chain is built.

they have to do is soak it up as fast as they can use it. Thus, the more surface, relative to body size, that a plant can expose to its seawater medium, the more efficient it is as an absorber of nutrients. And the smaller a body is, the greater its ratio of surface to volume. So two cells going their separate ways have more surface than a plant composed of two cells joined together, and the same rule applies for any number of cells to which you want to go. For this reason, life in the sea has encouraged the survival of plants of small size; there are no rewards for large size and complex structure, as there are for plants on land.

There *are* large plants in the sea; for example, such species as giant kelp, that grows to a length of 100 feet, but these are exceptions, unnecessary extravagances, and more than 99 percent of the sea's plant life is microscopic plankton. It differs basically from the green world ashore only in its unit size. As food for other creatures, plant plankton in effect is simply green grass already chewed up.

The plankton world is a bizarre, kaleidoscopic, miniature menagerie of fantastic shapes and colours. Its commonest members along the Pacific coast, as in most oceans, are various species of *diatoms,* yellow algae that may occur as single cells or as short chains of cells like strings of beads. Until recently the diatoms were regarded as simple plants, but many modern biologists now classify them as *protistans,* a kingdom of life that is neither plant nor animal but the primitive ancestors from which both plants and animals evolved. Despite their minute size, they are encased within shells of crystal-like silica on which are etched beautiful patterns that are used to distinguish several thousand diatom species around the world. Many of them have spines of silica protruding from their shells, making them look like tiny space satellites with projecting antennae. Another common group are the *dinoflagellates,* unicellular algae of a host of weird, spiked and fluted shapes with flailing, whip-like tails. And the plant or near-plant plankton kingdom has hordes more: shaped like balls, spindles, bells, pyramids, spirals; single cells, clusters of cells, chains of cells; with hair-like tails, feathery tails, without tails; transparent, yellow, green, red, and some of them phosphorescent. There are thousands of forms and species, so many that men have spent lifetimes studying them and have never seen them all.

The animal plankters are almost as numerous and varied. Many are microscopic, unicellular protozoans, more plant-like than animal; but most are crustaceans, miniature relatives of crabs and lobsters, with various arrangements of jointed legs, feelers and tails. The most numerous are *copepods,* shrimp-like crustaceans a little smaller than pinheads that propel themselves around in jerky fashion with oar-like feet. The copepod is probably the most abundant animal in the world; in fact, some marine biologists have said that it may outnumber *all* other animals combined. The sea's population of animal plankton is also swelled by swarms of microscopic larvae of larger sea animals like barnacles, snails, and oysters. It is a weird, wonderful, and lavish world indeed, including some of the most beautiful and bizarre of nature's creations, and a fully representative sample of it can exist in a single teaspoonful of seawater.

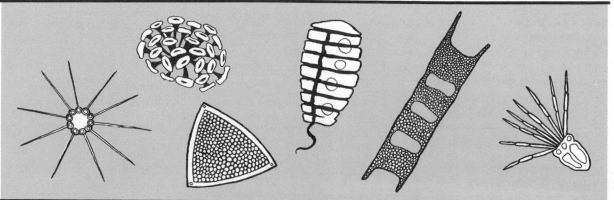

Plankton have bizarre shapes and a variety of colours. Most of the plant members are species of algae, the animal members are primarily shrimplike crustaceans. On these pages are diatoms and dinoflagellates, which are abundant species of algae; copepods, which are tiny crustaceans, and a potpourri of other diverse plankton forms.

From the sun to whales how food chains link the life of the sea

By eating and in turn being eaten, the vast galaxy of organisms that inhabit the sea pass the raw materials of life from one to another in endlessly repeating cycles known as food chains. The sea's many food chains interweave to produce a complex web as shown in this drawing. The small arrows indicate the channels by which food energy passes from animal to animal in a typical Pacific community from its deepwater zone (right), through a shallow-water zone (centre), to the shore (left), and into the air above. All food energy originates from the sun. As the large yellow arrows signify, sunlight is used by the sea's plant life to produce, through photosynthesis, the green foodstuff that supports all other oceanic species. Most of this primary production is performed by diatoms, microscopic algae which swarm in the surface layers. Other bottom and shore algae are also primary producers which provide an important food source in the particles of detritus that are created when they decay. These microscopic plant foods are screened out of the water and eaten by a horde of herbivores (plant eaters) like copepods, barnacles, clams, shrimps and small fish such as anchovies and needlefish. The herbivores are eaten by small carnivores (flesh eaters)—greycod, herring—and these in turn become food for large carnivores like salmon, seal, skate and killer whale. The food chains of the sea spill ashore through a variety of channels to feed land species like racoon, rat and many birds. Thus the whole community is inextricably bound together in an energy-flow web that can be traced back to its ultimate source—the sun.

98

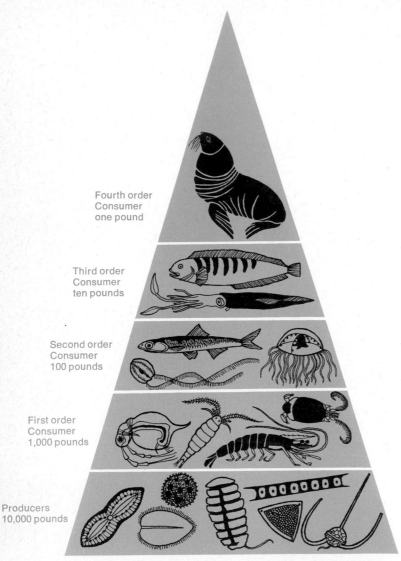

Fourth order
Consumer
one pound

Third order
Consumer
ten pounds

Second order
Consumer
100 pounds

First order
Consumer
1,000 pounds

Producers
10,000 pounds

Living things are able to convert only a tiny fraction of their food into living tissue, or individual weight gain. Over 90% of all food consumed goes for other purposes than a gain in weight. Thus in the illustration above the seal must eat the equivalent of 10,000 lbs. of plankton to gain one pound. Since the seal cannot eat plankton directly, it must eat 10 lbs. of fish, the fish in turn eat 100 lbs. of other animals, who must eat 1,000 lbs. of smaller plants and animals, who, finally, have to eat 10,000 lbs. of plankton.

The algal plankton, made up mainly of diatoms, is the basic fodder of the sea, the initial producer that combines the sunlight's energy, carbon dioxide, salts, and water into the green foodstuff that supports all the sea's larger life forms and the multi-million-dollar fishing industries of man. Someday it may be needed to save man's own exploding population from starving. Even most whales, the biggest of them 100 feet long and considerably larger than any dinosaur that ever existed, live on plankton alone simply by opening their mouths and straining plankton by the barrelful from the water flowing in.

Through food chains of eating and being eaten, the raw materials of life pass from plants to herbivores to small carnivores to large carnivores, and in this manner the stuff of life is used over and over again in an endless cycle. And in the sea, the first and basic link of every food chain is the algal plankton. Not only does it support all life *in* the sea, but also vast communities of bird and mammal life that live on the shore but derive their sustenance from the sea.

Food chains of the sea are almost endless in their diversity. Some samples for the Canadian Pacific coast are: diatom-copepod-herring-cod-shark, diatom-oyster-man, dinoflagellate-copepod-needlefish-salmon-grizzly bear, diatom-snail-sandpiper, diatom-copepod-shrimp-murrelet-peregrine falcon, copepod-pipefish-cormorant-cormorant egg-gull. Thinking up food chains is a game like doodling and could go on to fill pages. But the significant thing about it is that animals convert only about ten percent of their food into living tissue, so that each link in the chain has only one-tenth the aggregate body mass of the link below it. Thus, in the first food chain listed above, 10,000 pounds of diatoms would produce 1,000 pounds of copepods, then 100 pounds of herring, then 10 pounds of cod, and finally one pound of shark. The whole food chain structure can be likened to a pyramid with each level supporting a smaller number of larger animals in the level above.

But the microscopic diatom is well endowed to carry the whole pyramid on its spiny shoulders. They reproduce simply by cell division, one diatom splitting and becoming two about every 24 hours, with the result that a single diatom can have three billion descendants in a month. They need this astronomical reproductive capacity. A single copepod, itself almost microscopic, may have 120,000 diatoms in its stomach at one time. A herring may have 50,000 copepods in its stomach. And a hump-back whale, one of the fisheating whales, may eat a ton of herring, perhaps 5,000 fish, in a normal day's feeding. In other words, it is taking the product of 30,000,000,000,000 diatoms to sustain a hump-back whale for one day.

Hence, the little diatom, one of the most infinitesimal specks of living matter, unsung and largely unknown, perhaps neither plant nor animal but something between, is the workhorse and main source of food for the biggest living production line on earth.

---

12 THE EDGE OF THE SEA

To man, a land creature, the world of the sea may seem monotonously unvaried. It is just water. But look closer and you find as much variation in sea habitats as there is in the tropics-to-Arctic, desert-to-jungle life domains of the land.

There are, first of all, the two major and obvious divisions—the outer depths of the sea itself, and then the edge of the sea, with its beaches, mudflats, rocks and surf that make up the intertidal zone which changes daily from water to air with the coming and going of the tides. But within these two strikingly different worlds, a vast patchwork of smaller, distinctive life zones exist, more invisible cages, created by differences in water temperature, depths, salinity, light penetration, bottom and shore types, and the length of daily exposure to air that the tides produce.

The intertidal zone is a life domain of rich and fascinating bounty. It is a world that teems with life, wonderful adaptations, brilliant colours, and ingenious camouflages, including many animals that live fixed lives more like plants.

Of all the world's temperate seashores, that of the Canadian and American north Pacific has the greatest variety of species. For example, there are some 90 species of starfish between California and Alaska, but only about 20 on the corresponding shores of the Atlantic; 51 endemic Pacific *Spirontocaris* shrimps, three Atlantic; six Pacific *Cancer* Crabs, one Atlantic; and the list could go on and on. This is because the north Pacific has had a longer history as a temperate ocean (the north Atlantic went through a tropical phase about 50 million years ago) which has given the Pacific more time for the evolution of a variety of species adapted to the ocean conditions that prevail today.

The intertidal area between lowest and highest tides may be only a few tens of feet in width, but it is a zone of many worlds. It may be smooth rock, jumbled boulders, sand or mud, each of which creates different living conditions and attracts its own distinctive animals. But a more important creator of life zones is the duration of the flooding each day by the tides. At the lowest level there is a strip of shore exposed only briefly at low tide. At each successive higher point up the shore, the period of each day during which it is covered by tides keeps decreasing, and the length of exposure to air between the tides keeps increasing. At the highest tide mark, there is a zone that is dry land most of the time and flooded by sea only briefly each day when the tide is at its maximum. Finally there is a splash zone reached only by the spray of waves. Each of these has its one characteristic community of species, determined by the amount of exposure to air that the various seashore animals can endure.

Thus, the variations of rock, boulders, sand, mud and intertidal levels produce an infinite variety of aquatic and semi-aquatic habitats—places for swimmers, crawlers, burrowers, and sitters. And it is this that has produced the great diversity of life that inhabits the edge of the sea, because nature, given the time, invariably "invents" forms of life to exploit every different niche of habitat that is available.

One system of classifying them all is in terms of how they get around. The hosts of plankton, microscopic plants and animals that teem in every spoonful of seawater and make up the basic fodder of the sea, simply drift helplessly with tides and currents and have little control over their movements. Many others such as barnacles and oysters start life as helpless drifters or limited swimmers, but soon find a parking spot, attach themselves to rocks or wharf piles and spend the rest of their lives growing in one spot like a plant. These, the sitters, are the most abundant of seashore animals, after the plankton, because seawater is always moving, and in the sea it is a highly successful way of life simply to sit still and let the water bring the food instead of using energy by moving around after it. Many worms, clams and even some fish burrow in the intertidal mud or sand, and though not as fixed as the sitters, most of them live out their lives moving very little. Others such as starfish, snails and crabs are crawlers and creepers, most of them slowpokes and limited travellers. Finally, in the outer sea, there are the real travellers, the fish, whales, porpoises and seals, many of which travel tens of thousands of miles in their lifetime.

To describe all this varied and multitudinous life would require volumes. We can only consider here a few of the most abundant and obvious species that will be encountered in a seashore walk.

The first thing that will attract attention will be the little, whitish, conical shells that are packed together in thousands on rocks and wharves in a band just beneath the high-tide line. They may appear at first to be just jagged projections of the rock itself, but examine them when the tide is covering them, and you discover that each little cone has a feathery hand sweeping back and forth rhythmically through a trap door in the shell's top. They are animals, very much alive and kicking, not inanimate knobs of rock. You are meeting the barnacle, the most abundant of the seashore sitters, and one of the intertidal zone's most interesting creatures. He builds himself an impregnable wigwam of limy shell and lives a stay-at-home life inside, standing on his head and kicking food into his mouth with his feet.

Barnacles start life as minute, swimming shrimp-like larvae, sometimes so numerous they cloud the sea. After a period of growth they settle onto some solid object, cement themselves to it so firmly they can never move again, and secrete the shell around them. Sometimes they settle so densely, one atop another, that when small there can be 4,000 of them in a square foot. When the tide goes out, leaving them exposed to air, a series of plates like sliding doors close the tops of the shells and each barnacle waits in its snug, water-filled home for the tide to return. When the tide comes back, the rooftop door opens and the legs pop out and begin sweeping the water like miniature casting nets for the plankton that is always there. It is a highly efficient method of feeding, for vast numbers live where the tide covers them for only an hour or so a day, and some even survive where the only seawater that reaches them is the splash of waves.

There are about 25 species of barnacles in British Columbia waters, and identifying them is a technical study; however, there are two main groups that are readily distinguished. The omnipresent ones that look like miniature volcano cones are acorn barnacles. They endure the hammering of surf by cementing themselves to a solid base and presenting a rigid structure to the waves. The other group, known as the goose barnacles, have developed flexible, rubbery stalks which let them "roll with the punch" and absorb wave impacts in this manner. The goose barnacle, at the end of its stalk, is flattened, clam-like, with white or bluish shell plates, and looks very different from the cone-shaped acorn barnacles.

There are two main clans of seashore dwellers: the crustaceans which include crabs, shrimps and many plankton forms, and the mollusks or shellfish which include snails, clams, oysters, scallops and mussels. The barnacle, despite his shell which is usually a mollusk trademark, is a crustacean. But two other common intertidal sitters—the oyster and blue mussel—are mollusks. They are known as bivalve mollusks because they have two hinged shells or "valves" which fit together like a suitcase. (Snails and their like, with a single shell, are univalves.)

The blue mussel has brilliant blue, clam-like shells up to two inches long and attaches itself in an upright position to rocks, wharves or gravel with fibrous threads that radiate outward like guy wires. Like the barnacle, it forms masses so dense that it hides the rock or piling to which it is fastened. It is an animal of the middle tide zone where it gets longer periods of submergence than barnacles which are concentrated in the upper shore.

Oysters, distinguished from their clam relatives by their rough, irregular shells, attach themselves by lying flat and cementing the lower shell to a rock or a bed of other oyster shells, leaving the hinged upper shell movable. Over a period of years, the cemented masses of shells build up thick oyster "reefs." There are several native, Pacific-coast oysters, but they are all small, and the commercial oyster of the North American Pacific is the bigger Japanese oyster first imported in the 1930's. Wild populations of the Japanese oyster are established at many points along the B.C. coast, and it now ranks as a thoroughly naturalized citizen.

Nature makes sure that there are plenty of oyster progeny to populate all the oyster living space available. One female oyster can release over a hundred million eggs two or three

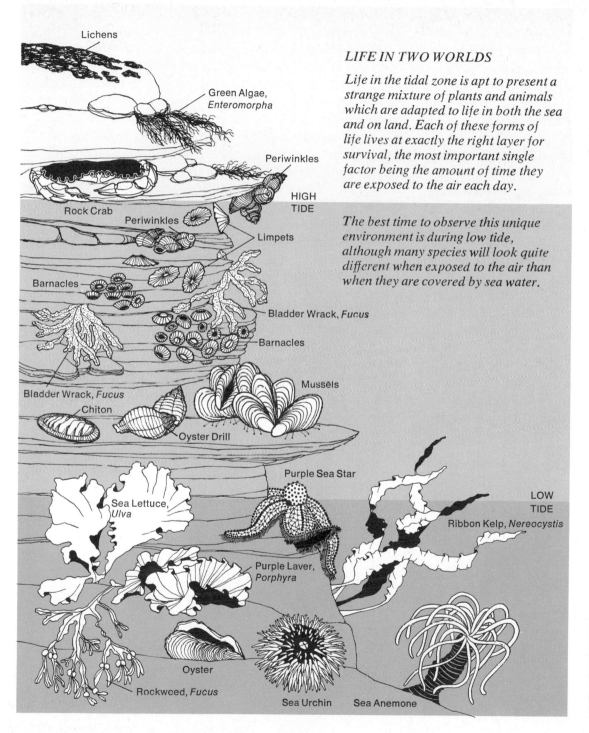

Lichens

Green Algae, *Enteromorpha*

Periwinkles

Rock Crab

Periwinkles

Limpets

Barnacles

Bladder Wrack, *Fucus*

Barnacles

HIGH TIDE

Bladder Wrack, *Fucus*

Chiton

Oyster Drill

Mussels

Sea Lettuce, *Ulva*

Purple Sea Star

Purple Laver, *Porphyra*

LOW TIDE

Ribbon Kelp, *Nereocystis*

Oyster

Rockweed, *Fucus*

Sea Urchin

Sea Anemone

LIFE IN TWO WORLDS

Life in the tidal zone is apt to present a strange mixture of plants and animals which are adapted to life in both the sea and on land. Each of these forms of life lives at exactly the right layer for survival, the most important single factor being the amount of time they are exposed to the air each day.

The best time to observe this unique environment is during low tide, although many species will look quite different when exposed to the air than when they are covered by sea water.

Specimens of sea plants are easy to collect — float the plant in water and slide a piece of heavy paper underneath.

Slowly lift the paper when the specimen is in the centre.

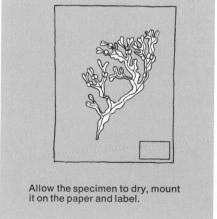

Allow the specimen to dry, mount it on the paper and label.

times a year, and if all the offspring of one female plus their descendants survived for five years there would be a mass of oysters 250 times the volume of the earth. But few microscopic oyster larvae escape being eaten by larger sea animals, and few of these in turn succeed in finding a parking spot where they can grow into mature oysters. One thousand may settle on one old oyster shell, 999 will die from crowding and competition, and in the end only one will survive.

Mussels and oysters feed by filtering plankton (including vast numbers of their own larvae) from the water that passes over their gills, so that breathing and feeding are accomplished in a single operation. One fullgrown mussel filters plankton from about 50 quarts of water a day and provides a graphic example of the tremendous productivity of the sea. An acre of mussels standing shell to shell puts on 40,000 pounds of weight a year, three-quarters of which is shell, but the remaining 10,000 pounds is highly edible and nutritious meat. For comparison, an acre of good pasture land produces about 200 pounds of beef per year—one fiftieth of the meat production from a good mussel bed.

The strangest and most beautiful of all the intertidal sitters are the sea anemones. It is always a shock to the novice seashore explorer to learn that these colourful, benign-looking beauties with their crowns of brilliant, petal-like tentacles are not the underwater flowers they appear to be, but voracious, carnivorous animals.

There are several sea anemone species that vary widely in size, form and colour, but all of them are graceful, delicate and gorgeously hued—unrivalled as the most beautiful animals of the sea. They have round, leathery bodies that in some species are squat and low, in others graceful waving columns up to a foot high, and the tops are always crowned with blossom-like circlets of tentacles that resemble exotic flowers. A common sea anemone colour is vivid green, but they are also white, yellow, orange, red, and a variety of intermediary browns, pinks and lavenders.

The brilliant tentacles have stinging spines which stun small animals swimming near; the food thus obtained is passed to the mouth at the centre of the tentacle ring and sucked into the stomach. The sting is usually too slight to be felt by the human skin, but with large sea anemones it can be detected as a slight tingling. It is the anemone's feeding ways that reveal it to be a voracious animal and not a plant. It can swallow a small crab and in fifteen minutes digest the meat, spit out the bits of indigestible shell, and be ready for another meal. Its digesting enzymes are so potent that a tarnished penny inserted into its stomach will be ejected polished and shiny in less than an hour. When danger threatens, or the tide goes out exposing a sea

The sea anemones are really animals which catch unwary fish which swim too close.

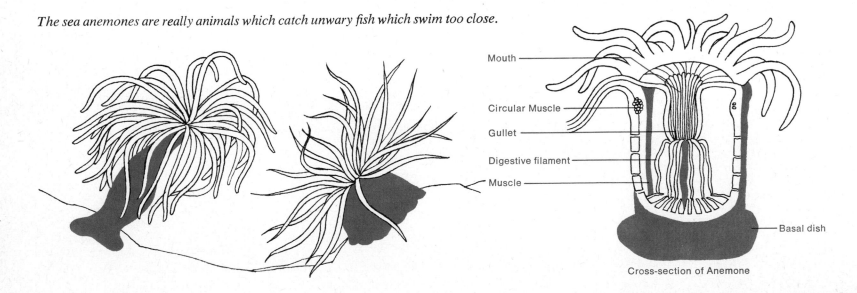

Mouth

Circular Muscle

Gullet

Digestive filament

Muscle

Basal dish

Cross-section of Anemone

anemone to air, it tucks its tentacles inside its body and contracts into a wrinkled, slimy-looking little stump, its splendid finery, like Cinderella's at midnight, suddenly gone.

Barnacles, oysters, mussels and sea anemones are some of the most obvious sitters who let the tides do the work of bringing the food to them. But there are other ways of intertidal life, those of the burrowers and crawlers.

13 BURROWERS AND CRAWLERS

Every overturned rock or spadeful of intertidal sand reveals a scuttling, squirming community of burrowers and crawlers.

There is a host of burrowing snails, mud shrimps, ghost shrimps, sand hoppers, even a burrowing anemone, and a weird array of tunnelling worms. Some come up to the surface when the tide is in and burrow out of sight when the tide recedes; some come out only at night, and dig in for the day. Some bury themselves and live on the organic matter mixed with the sand; but most keep tiny burrows open to the surface, and feed on plankton from the water flowing in.

The marine worms are a motley crew. The plume worm lives in a parchment-like tube from which a bright red or green ring of gill and feeding filaments protrude like small sea anemones; the delicate plumes are so light-sensitive that they snap back into the tube for protection if just a shadow passes over them. On southern Pacific beaches, the famous lancelet worm is uncatchable and usually just glimpsed, because it can burrow through wet sand as fast as a fish can swim. Another worm, up to 20 inches long, is such a sloppy housekeeper and leaves so much food in its burrow that it always has a number of boarders—worms, small crabs and fish—that move in and live luxuriously on the leftovers; appropriately, it is known as the innkeeper worm.

But the burrowers that provide the most interesting challenge for a curious naturalist who wants to name things are the clams. There is a large number of species, good identification guides are available, and all of them are readily identifiable by their shells.

Most clams keep hidden under mud or sand, usually at low tide levels where there are only brief exposures to air. There they sit with a fleshy siphon tube running up to the surface through which they keep pumping in water for both feeding and breathing. The tip of the siphon is obscured by sand and difficult to detect, but clams are stupid and inconsistent about their hiding, because periodically, when the siphon becomes clogged with sand, they flush it out by pumping a jet of water through it that

Many animals live just below the surface of the sand, some simply cover themselves while others dig elaborate tunnels. The razor clam is one of the fastest burrowers; the sand lance is a burrowing fish.

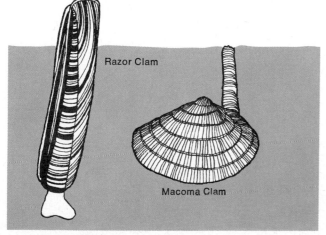

Razor Clam

Macoma Clam

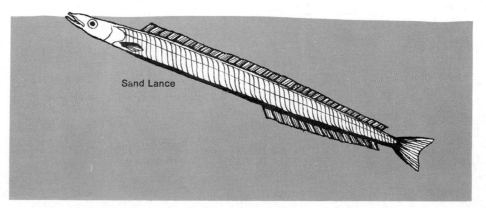

Sand Lance

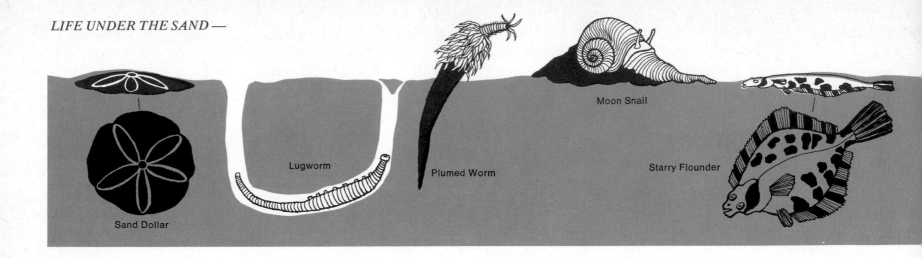

Sand Dollar

Lugworm

Plumed Worm

Moon Snail

Starry Flounder

spouts like a small geyser. On a good clam beach, these geysers can be seen spurting all around, each one betraying the hiding place of a clam that should know better. Occasionally a clam, disturbed by a foot tread, will perform the ultimate in audacity and stupidity by sending a jet of cold water up a searching clam-digger's pant leg.

Clams burrow by extending a fleshy foot between the shells, expanding it with blood until it forms a swollen anchor, then pulling themselves forward into the hole the foot has made in the sand. It sounds clumsy and slow, but some clams have perfected it into a rapid method of getting places. The high-speed champion is the razor clam, a streamlined tunneller up to six inches long who, if laid on the sand, will bury itself in half a dozen seconds. If you don't get a razor clam with your first or second shovelful, give up, because by that time the clam will be so deep you'll never catch up to it in the oozing sand. The largest Canadian Pacific clam, the geoduck (goo-ee-duck), is up to nine inches long, burrows to three feet, and has a siphon tube that can reach the surface from this depth.

The various clam species differ greatly in their burrowing prowess. Some, known as piddocks, are literally borers rather than burrowers, for they bore with rasping shells into soft rock. Piddocks start boring a home when small and keep enlarging its interior as they grow until they wind up imprisoned for life in a chamber with an entrance hole smaller than they are.

The fast diggers like the razor clam can live where pounding surf is constantly shifting the sand because they can keep ahead of the sand movements, whereas slow diggers have to live where the sand is stable. Good diggers can live in hard-packed sand or clay, poor diggers only in soft mud–invisible cages again, with every species in its prescribed place.

Surely the most unexpected intertidal burrower, however, is the sandlance–unexpected, because it's a fish! Known also as needlefish, they are one of the most abundant fish of the British Columbia coast. Plankton eaters, they form one of the most important links in food chains of the inshore waters, in fact they are so sought after by larger fish and fish-eating birds that to escape enemies they frequently burrow into the sand under shallow water, leaving only their heads exposed for breathing. Then, frequently, the tide goes out and leaves the sandlances high and dry. But this is no crisis, for they simply burrow a little deeper and wait in the wet sand for the tide to return. However, if it is a hot day and the sand begins to dry, or if the exposure between tides is long, the sandlances get tired of waiting, wriggle up to the surface and start flapping their way back down to the sea. Once caught in this predicament, it's a lucky sandlance that makes it back to its briny home, because there are too many fish-relishing gulls and shore-birds always on the watch for sand-lance dinners.

Our final intertidal clan is the creepers and crawlers–the snails, crabs and starfish.

The snails, like their relatives the clams, are a good study for

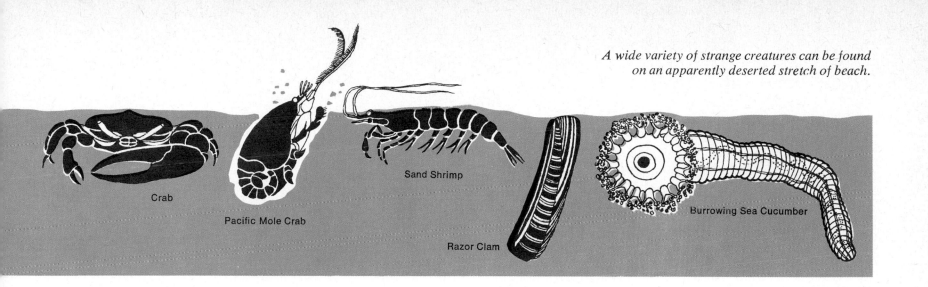

Crab

Pacific Mole Crab

Sand Shrimp

Razor Clam

Burrowing Sea Cucumber

amateurs, for their shells identify them. Canada's west coast has a rich variety of them—the limpets with shells like little Chinese coolie hats, the spiralled whelks, the abalone with its rainbow-hued, mother-of-pearl interior decorating job. In size they range from the tiny quarter-inch margarite and chink-shell to the moon snail as big as a grapefruit.

There are no lobsters on the Pacific coast, to the surprise and disappointment of visiting gourmets, but the crabs are an abundant and delectable substitute. The common, big, reddish-brown, commercial crab of the Pacific can grow to a diameter of nine inches. Watch out for the big toothed pincers, because a husky specimen can almost take off a finger.

There are numerous other smaller crabs. One group—the long-legged spider crabs—are known also as decorator crabs because they plant a variety of seaweeds on their shells for camouflage and turn themselves into walking gardens. Most crabs can be grasped safely across the middle of the back, but the decorator, to tend his garden, has pincers that can reach backward.

The hermit crabs are another group of clever innovators. They are cursed with soft, vulnerable, shell-less abdomens. To protect himself each hermit crab takes over an empty snail shell and walks around with the shell on his back, only his armoured head, legs and threatening claws exposed. When an enemy attacks, the hermit retreats completely into his borrowed fortress and sits out the siege. It works fine until the little crab grows too big for his portable house, then he has to vacate and scurry

around until he finds a bigger shell. He knows full well his vulnerability on these occasions, and the hermit crab is probably the fastest house hunter living—no arguments about leases, he just gets a roof over that tender abdomen as fast as he can.

One of the most abundant items of jetsam on every beach are empty crab shells. Beaches are sometimes littered with thousands of them. It doesn't mean some deadly epidemic is killing all the crabs, it merely indicates that the crabs are dressing up in a new suit. Periodically they have to shuck off their shells to make room for new growth. When the fit starts getting too tight, a crab's shell splits along the hind edge, the crab shrinks himself by expelling fluid from his body, and simply backs out of the outgrown shell. The new shell underneath is soft, so the crab soaks up a new supply of seawater enlarging his body and stretching the shell to a more comfortable size.

But the creepers that invariably attract the most attention are starfish. Colourful, with attractive, symmetical shapes that are highly photogenic on colour film, the starfish are favourites of naturalists and beachcombers. They are so slow-moving that they are often stranded by falling tides in rock pools or at higher points up the beach where they are sitting it out, waiting for the tide's return. The B.C. coast has more shapes, sizes, and colours of starfish than any other coast on earth. Many a novice beachcomber finds it difficult to accept that these brilliant and beautiful forms are animals; but they are, and like the sea anemones, in their plodding, obtuse way they are vicious killers.

Starfish consist of a central disk or body with several arms or "rays" radiating outward. Usually there are five arms, giving them a starlike form, but some species have as many as 24 like the petals of a flower. The under surfaces of the arms are covered with hundreds of tiny, suction-tipped feet that function with a complex hydraulic pressure system of arteries and valves. Water pumped in through a filter fills the tube feet, and then by pumping it out again the suction is obtained. A large starfish can adhere to a rock so firmly that it can withstand a pull of 100 pounds, and when torn free many of the little sucker-like feet break off and remain stuck to the rock. They move by reaching out with the minuscule feet, attaching the suction tips, then contracting them to draw the body forward. In this manner they glide along an inch or two a minute, so slowly the movement is barely detectable to the eye.

Lacking speed, eyes, jaws and teeth, starfish obtain their food through a combination of sightless hunting, brute strength and a bizarre capacity for turning their stomachs inside out. Their main food is clams and they are serious predators of oyster beds. When a starfish bumps into a clam, it wraps its arms around the clam's shell, attaches the suckered feet, then applies a steady pull until the clam's muscles tire and the two shells begin to open. The starfish's mouth is in the centre of its under surface, and when the clam shells separate, the starfish extrudes its stomach inside out through the mouth and into the clam, and the clam dinner is digested outside the starfish's body. The ways of life of the sea have some grotesque aberrations.

Starfish are hard to kill. If one loses an arm or two, the body grows new arms, and under some circumstances the detached arms can grow a new body. Before this was known, Japanese oyster raisers used to remove starfish from their oyster beds, cut them in two and toss them back—but they were only making two starfish each time out of one.

The commonest British Columbia species is the purple starfish, six to 20 inches across, which sometimes belies its name by being yellow, orange or brown. There are numerous others, pink, blood red, green, blue and grey, pure coloured and mottled, large and small, long-armed, short-armed, and all are identifiable by an amateur with a good marine-life guide. The largest is the sunflower star, which can have up to 24 arms, and can be almost a yard across.

Starfish have some eccentric relatives—sea urchins, covered with brightly coloured spines like tiny, rolled-up porcupines; sand dollars, with flat, circular shells that have a star pattern etched on their tops to indicate their starfish family tree; and sea cucumbers, colourful slug-like animals with a rosette of feeding tentacles.

The ocean world teems with a fauna so much more abundant and varied than that of the land that we have hardly begun to cover it all. From microscopic plankton to the 100-ton blue whale, it is a fauna staggering in its immensity, multiformity and contrast. It is as though evolution went berserk and didn't know where to stop when it discovered the fertile, diverse and limitless living space of the sea.

14 WANDERING WAIFS OF THE DISTANT SEA

The food wealth of the sea, founded on its astronomical production of plankton, spills ashore through devious food chains to feed vast communities of animals that live over and beside the sea in addition to those in it.

A few of these alien exploiters of the sea are mammals. Coastal grizzly bears feed heavily on salmon when these fish are entering their spawning streams. River otters, mink and raccoons hunt along seashores and live on its intertidal life. Sea otters, now extinct along the B.C. coast but still surviving in Californian and Alaskan waters, are mammals like the seals and sea lions that spend most of their lives at sea.

By far the largest number of land-based species that have become adapted to and dependent on the sea are birds. Some use the sea for only parts of each year; others, the genuine seabirds, never leave the ocean and therefore are major seashore attractions for visiting naturalists from inland regions.

The shorebirds—sandpipers, plovers and oystercatchers—comprise a large clan that flock along seashores probing mud or sand for intertidal life. About 25 species frequent the Pacific coast with some degree of regularity, but most of these nest in the Arctic and winter farther south, and appear along our coast just in spring and fall during migration. A few are Pacific coast endemics that occur nowhere else in Canada. Only one, the black oystercatcher, is a coastal nester and year-round resident. Other shorebirds that nest in Alaska or Siberia and appear as migrants or winterers on the British Columbia coast but almost never inland are the surf bird, black turnstone, wandering tattler, rock sandpiper and sharp-tailed sandpiper.

The waterfowl–swans, geese and ducks–are obviously well-adapted water birds, but not authentic seabirds. They nest on freshwater lakes and marshes of the B.C. interior, the prairies and the Arctic, but vast numbers of them fly out to the coast to winter on the sea. Thirty-four species occur along the British Columbia coast more or less regularly, some of them shallow-water feeders on marine plants, others adept deep-water divers for fish and sea-bottom animals. West coast specialties, rare or absent elsewhere in Canada, are the black brant, emperor goose, white-fronted goose, cinnamon teal (a southerner that reaches the northern limits of its range in southern B.C.), European widgeon, Barrow's goldeneye, harlequin duck, surf and common scoters.

Loons and grebes, eight west coast species, are in the same category as ducks and geese–they are inland, freshwater nesters that winter along the coast. They are skilled and rapid underwater swimmers, and catch fish easily. Species more easily found and seen on the west coast than anywhere else in Canada are the Arctic loon, eared grebe and western grebe.

The most abundant and obvious seabirds are gulls; most of them, like the waterfowl, are also inland nesters that only winter on the sea. Only one species, the glaucous-winged gull, is a coastal nester and year-round resident. Familiar seashore scavengers and ship followers, the gulls are birds that everyone recognizes at least as "sea-gulls," but when it comes to sorting out the 12 rather lookalike species that may appear on the B.C. coast, the novice may give up in despair and even the experienced student of birds faces a challenge. Some species are so similar they have to be identified by a system of elimination that relies on small differences in leg and bill colours. Their identification is further complicated by the fact that most gull species have nondescript dark grey plumages for their first two years and do not acquire the white and pearly grey adult plumages until they are three years old.

The glaucous-winged, a true "sea-gull" that rarely strays inland, is probably the commonest Pacific coast bird, abundant in winter even in cities and towns. Its identification marks are grey wingtips, rather than black, as most gulls have. It is one bird that has prospered and grown more abundant with the growth of human population. Winter is a critical time for intertidal-feeding birds like gulls because the lowest and best food-producing winter tides occur at night when the birds cannot take advantage of them. Winter mortality among shore-scavenging gulls is high for this reason–but not for the glaucous-winged. This species, a versatile scavenger, has learned to utilize the rich food sources of man's garbage dumps and the refuse from fishing

All gulls are expert flyers —Bonaparte's gull here nearly turns a somersault as he dives below the water to catch a fish near the surface.

fleets and canneries, and has even learned to raid bird-lovers' backyard feeding stations. As a result, its winter survival rate is high and its population has increased with the spread of man along the Pacific coast.

Another gull that is a special west coast attraction for bird-watchers is the mew or short-billed gull, an example of a bird that almost established a round-the-world range during the shakeup of bird dispersal after the Ice Age, but didn't quite make it. Its range extends from Iceland and Europe, where it is known as the common gull, eastward across Siberia and down the west coast of North America, but it has never been able to close the gap between western Canada and Iceland to make its range circumpolar. It is a small, attractive gull (fieldmarks: unmarked, yellowish-green bill and legs) and many Canadian birdwatchers who are familiar with it in ornithological literature as Europe's common gull are unaware that the west coast's mew gull is the same bird. It nests inland but nonbreeders remain on the coast all summer, and it is second only to the glaucous-winged in abundance.

Two other gulls that are sought by Canadian birdwatchers are the western gull and Heermann's gull, because they are southern nesters that defy the usual bird migration pattern by migrating *northward* into British Columbia waters for the fall and winter.

The bald eagle and peregrine falcon are land birds found all over North America (the peregrine around the world), but their Pacific coast populations have adopted such sea-oriented lives that they rank a prominent place in the seabird fraternity. The peregrine falcon, known also as duck hawk and Peale's falcon, is a bird killer and on the Pacific it is always associated with and feeds on small fish-eating seabirds, mainly murrelets and auklets, in this way getting all its sustenance secondhand from the sea. The bald eagle is largely a beach scavenger, feeding on dead marine life cast up by the sea, only occasionally capturing live fish and birds. These sea-exploiting ways of life are highly successful, for both these birds of prey have become very rare everywhere else, believed to be the victims of widespread pesticide spraying, but they are still abundant on the Pacific which has become their last stronghold.

The peregrine, one of the most cosmopolitan of birds, has been trained for hunting and prized by falconers in Asia and Europe since ancient times. It is more abundant in the Queen Charlottes, where about 75 pairs nest, than anywhere else in the world. There are places in the Queen Charlottes where one can have six peregrine eyries in view at once, an experience no other spot on earth can duplicate. Falconers from all over North America and Europe have for years made pilgrimages to the Queen Charlottes, lowered themselves down the precarious cliffs on ropes and taken young peregrines from the eyries to train for falconry. This practice was regulated by the British Columbia Fish and Wildlife Branch and the taking of young falcons was allowed only by government permit. But with the peregrine on the verge of extinction everywhere else, and with the residues of deadly pesticides spreading through the oceans of the world, government permits for the capture of young peregrines are no longer being issued, and the unique Queen Charlotte falcon population is under rigid protection.

The bald eagle is a conspicuous bird of the Pacific shore and figured prominently in Indian myths and legends. There is no evidence of an eagle decline here as there is everywhere else in North America. David Hancock, a biologist who has studied them intimately, flying his own aircraft to locate and observe them, estimates there are 7,000 to 10,000 pairs nesting on the B.C. coast. Sometimes 20 eagles can be seen concentrated around a beached whale or seal carcass. One pair produces young most years in Vancouver's Stanley Park, another in West Vancouver's Lighthouse Park, another at Elk Lake on the outskirts of Victoria.

Another land bird closely linked to the sea is the northwestern crow, the small coastal species of crow. It is a common beachcomber and a predator of seabird nesting colonies, usually present and waiting for an opportunity to snatch eggs or young from seabird nests whenever the nests are left unguarded.

The cormorants are more sea-living than any of the preceding birds, but still not full-blown seabirds, for they spend much time resting ashore. They are large black birds and are abundant in the British Columbia waters throughout the year. Expert divers and underwater swimmers, they pursue fish to great depths—dives to almost 200 feet have been recorded. They nest in colonies, often with other seabirds, on cliff ledges, rocky inlets, and occasionally in low trees. The British Columbia coast has three species. The doublecrested cormorant occurs all across

Canada, nesting on inland lakes as well as Atlantic and Pacific coasts. The other two–Brandt's cormorant and pelagic cormorant–are Pacific endemics. (Pelagic, meaning open ocean far from land, is a misnomer; it is a coastal bird.) Pelagic cormorants are widespread nesters and are found at many points along the Canadian coast north to the Queen Charlottes. Brandt's cormorants, though common in southern British Columbia waters, nest mainly to the south. Until 1965 they were not believed to nest anywhere in Canada, but that year the first Canadian nesting colony was discovered on a small island off Wickaninnish Provincial Park, on the outer coast of Vancouver Island, by David Stirling, Frank Buffam and R. Y. Edwards, British Columbia park naturalists.

Now we reach the genuine seabirds–birds so attached to the sea that they spend their entire lives there except for brief periods each summer when they use a cliff or islet beside the sea for nesting. Some so distrust the land that even at breeding times they come ashore to change nesting partners only at night. Some are so helpless off the water that they cannot even land on anything solid, and to reach their nests ashore they use the unusual method of flying at full tilt into trees or bushes to reduce their flight speed and then let themselves tumble through the cushioning branches to the ground beneath. For them, every landing is a crash landing, and this practice, night after night throughout the breeding season, must produce more bruises and bodily wear and tear than any other procedure in the whole punishing and strenuous gamut of bird aeronautics.

Canada's Pacific seabirds can be lumped into two groups– those that nest on land and can be seen along the coast with some degree of regularity, and the pelagic birds of the faraway, open sea that nest elsewhere, winter as oceanic wanderers far from land, and come close to our shores only as rare and unwilling storm-blown castaways.

In the first group are seven species of the Alcid family–the murres, guillemots, murrelets, auklets and puffins. The alcids are not the obvious, close-to-shore birds that gulls and cormorants are, but they are often within telescope or binocular range of shore. Since they can only be seen on the sea, they are eagerly sought by visiting naturalists. Most of them move to more northern parts of the coast to nest and are most likely to be seen in southern waters around Vancouver in fall, winter and spring.

Crows are one of the most fearless of birds — here they attack an eagle, a traditional enemy.

Alcids are quaint, black and white birds, smaller than ducks, with legs far back on their bodies for efficient swimming, which gives them an upright, penguin-like posture on the rare occasions that they are seen on land around their nests. They have short, narrow wings that beat rapidly and produce a buzzing flight suggestive of big bumblebees.

Unlike other water birds, which use only their feet for swimming, the alcids use their wings and literally "fly" underwater.

They dive from air directly underwater without pausing on the surface, and their wings appear to continue beating without missing a stroke. They are swift and can manoeuvre beneath the water, catching fish as easily as a swallow catches gnats; the most skilled diving ducks and loons are clumsy and slow in comparison. This underwater at-homeness is a frustrating annoyance for birdwatchers, because the alcids are frequently on the surface so briefly that it is difficult to locate them with binoculars and identify them before they are down again.

The most frequently seen British Columbia alcid is the common murre, yet only one breeding colony is known—on Triangle Island off the northern tip of Vancouver Island, where about 3,000 nest. Probably many of British Columbia's abundant wintering murres are from Alaskan and Californian nesting colonies. The common murre also occurs on the Atlantic, but all the other alcids are confined to the Pacific.

The pigeon guillemot nests all along the coast, including many islets around Victoria and Vancouver, where it can be seen throughout the year.

The marbled murrelet, although it is the mystery bird whose nest has never been found, is also fairly common throughout the year along the whole coast.

The ancient murrelet nests on the Queen Charlottes and disappears from the southern coast during the summer.

The remaining three alcids are less frequently seen. The tufted puffin, a weirdo with a huge, triangular, orange-red bill and drooping head crest, has numerous nesting localities along the coast, but they disappear after nesting and most of them are believed to winter as pelagic birds far out at sea. Cassin's auklet and rhinoceros auklet nest from northern Vancouver Island northward and along the Washington coast just south of the Canadian border. Washington-nesting birds may wander up into southern Strait of Georgia waters during their nesting season, and these two auklets also appear on the southern B.C. coast as migrating or wintering rarities.

Two other seabirds that share nesting colonies with the alcids are fork-tailed and Leach's petrels, dark, robin-sized birds, the "Mother Carey's chickens" of mariners' folklore. Though common, they are rarely seen, because they approach their nests only at night and spend the days foraging for food well out at sea, avoiding shore waters.

We will return to the alcids and petrels in the next chapter when we examine the community life and interrelationships of a seabird nesting colony. But for this chapter's survey of seabird species, we still have the pelagic birds of the open ocean.

The main pelagic species are the various albatrosses and shearwaters which are among the most romantic and fascinating of all birds. Most of them nest on tiny, remote, oceanic islands in the southern hemisphere but spend most of their lives as wandering waifs in midocean, so fearful of land that sometimes they exhaust themselves and die when struggling to stay at sea against gales blowing them toward shore. They appear in northern oceans of the world during our summers as wintering birds escaping the southern hemisphere winters. Usually they are seen only from ships at sea, rarely from land.

They are uniquely adapted for a life on the open ocean. They have salt glands that assist the kidneys in filtering salt from the blood, which permits them to drink saltwater. And they have huge wing surfaces in relation to body weight which enables them to spend hours in effortless soaring, using wind currents deflected upward off wavecrests for aerodynamic lift. The wandering albatross, 11 feet from wingtip to wingtip, has the greatest wingspan of any bird. It is believed that these pelagic species soar and adjust to changing air currents so subconsciously that they even sleep on the wing. They must also possess superb navigating skills, because after wandering the trackless oceans for months without opportunity to see land, they converge unerringly, some species on the same day year after year, on the tiny midocean islets where they nest. In fact, while they are immature birds too young to breed, they spend several years at sea, never touching land.

Three north Pacific pelagic wanderers that often follow ships and fishing boats to within 10 to 15 miles of shore but rarely nearer are the black-footed albatross, sooty shearwater and fulmar. Four others, considerably rarer, are the pink-footed manx, pale-footed and slender-billed shearwaters. But of all these, only two—the sooty shearwater and fulmar—come near shore with any regularity, a few usually turning up each year around Victoria or in the Strait of Georgia during or following storms. Victoria, because it is nearer the open ocean, gets more of these pelagic wanderers than Vancouver.

There are many seabird observation points around both

cities, but two are especially good. Active Pass, the narrow scenic channel between Mayne and Galiano Islands, traversed several times a day by the Vancouver-Victoria ferries, has frequent tide-produced upwellings of water that bring marine life to the surface and attract large numbers of seabirds at all times of the year except midsummer. Sometimes Active Pass swarms with thousands of loons, cormorants, gulls, murres, and western grebes. The other rich attracter of seabirds is Clover Point, near Victoria's Beacon Hill Park, where naturalists have recorded 161 species of birds during the past ten years; when rare pelagic birds are seen, it is often here.

But the most pleasant and surest way of seeing seabirds is to take a summer cruise on one of the ships that ply the Inside Passage between Vancouver, Prince Rupert and Skagway, Alaska. Here, amidst the finest coastal scenery of the world, one can stand on deck with binoculars and watch a constant passing show of birds. Many inland nesters such as Arctic and red-throated loons, scoters and harlequin ducks have nonbreeding flocks summering at sea in these more northern waters. Glaucous-winged and mew gulls will follow the ship, providing an excellent opportunity to study at close range their distinguishing fieldmarks, and in late summer one might also see California, western and Heermann's gulls that have returned to the sea for their winter wanderings. Frequently a white speck on a bare tree stub ashore will materialize through binoculars into a bald eagle, its white head gleaming in the sun. Flocks of murres, murrelets, auklets, guillemots and petrels will dive or skitter across the water to open a path for your ship. The little fork-tailed petrel, rarely seen from land because it approaches even its nesting colonies only at night, may be common in the open sea.

But the major lure are the pelagic species that one can seldom see except from a ship at sea. Three pelagics that are likely to be seen on this Pacific coast cruise in summer are fulmars, sooty shearwaters and black-footed albatrosses, and if your luck is running and your eyes are sharp you may also spot one or two of the rarer shearwaters. Dixon Entrance north of Prince Rupert sometimes has summer flocks of thousands of sooty shearwaters blackening the water and disappearing to the horizon like wispy clouds of smoke. If your main object is to look for birds, select a cruise schedule that will take you across the open-sea stretches of Queen Charlotte Sound and Dixon Entrance in daylight.

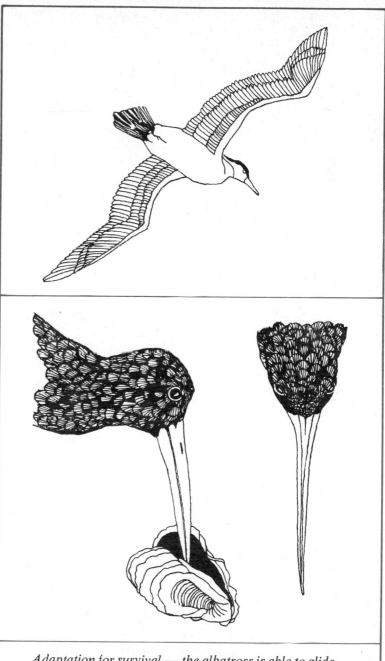

Adaptation for survival — the albatross is able to glide for long periods on its huge wings; the oystercatcher uses its chisel-like bill to pry open oyster shells.

A female eagle feeding her ever-hungry young.

A bald eagle nestling. This one is five weeks old.

*An adult bald eagle showing
the white head.*

Vanishing monarch

The Pacific coast is one of the few remaining refuges of the bald eagle. Its habitat varies from open areas to forests, but it is usually near water. Pairs may remain mated for life. Nests are made of sticks, twigs and debris, and are added to each year of use; some nests, used for more than 15 years, have weighed several tons. Where it can, the eagle prefers to rob osprey rather than catch its own fish.

right: This dark-plumaged, immature eagle will not acquire the white head and tail of maturity until it is about three years old.

15 SEABIRD APARTMENTS

A characteristic of seabirds is their habit of nesting together in dense, massed colonies.

Colony-nesting is rather rare among birds. Most birds nest singly and defend the territories around their nests against others of the same species, a practice that ensures each pair an exclusive hunting area from which to obtain food when the nestlings have to be fed. Colony-nesting is practised only by birds that use shifting, communal feeding grounds, such as swallows that feed on flying insects and have to follow the insect swarms from place to place, and seabirds that feed at sea, following the schools of fish.

In the case of seabirds, there are other reasons for colony-nesting. They require very specialized nesting locations. The nest sites have to be remote islands free of disturbance by man and predators such as rats and mink. Since most seabird species are incapable of taking wing from level ground, another requirement is a cliff from which they can pitch off into midair, or at least a steep slope to aid them in getting airborne. Some species require jumbles of loose boulders full of crannies in which to hide their nests, some nest only on flat, exposed, cliff ledges, several species dig burrows to hide their nests and therefore need areas of soil and turf. They must have abundant food in the sea nearby, a requirement that usually demands areas where tides and currents are moving surface waters away from shore and generating upwellings of bottom water. Bottom waters are highly fertile from settling nutrients and these upwellings create rich blooms of plankton which in turn support abundant reproduction of small fish. Nesting sites that combine all these requirements are rare and in demand, so where they occur they are usually shared by large numbers of seabirds of several species.

A seabird nesting colony may appear to be a chaotic melée of squabbling birds constantly conflicting and getting in each other's way. But actually it is order amidst apparent disorder, a classic example of how nature fits each species into its own ecological niche—its own way of making a living and reproducing its kind—thus ensuring that every way of life the environment offers is utilized without inefficient competition between species. So a seabird nesting cliff may look like a pandemonium of thousands of massed birds dotting its ledges and swarming back and forth between cliff and sea, yet on closer examination it reveals itself to be a segregated apartment block with each species occupying its own tier or apartments, separated from other species. For it is a basic rule of life that every species, simply to exist and escape extinction, must carve out a way of living that exploits its environment in a manner that is exclusively its own. Nowhere is this better illustrated than in a seabird nesting colony.

There are a few seabird nesting islands in southern B.C. waters that may be reached relatively easily by boat, but the largest and most dramatic are off northern Vancouver Island and the Queen Charlottes, remote and difficult of access. These northern nesting colonies are larger and have a greater variety of species because they are rarely disturbed by man, have higher and more precipitous cliffs, and are nearer the major feeding grounds of the open ocean.

The biggest and most varied colony on the inner south coast is tiny Mandarte Island in the Strait of Georgia off Sidney where some 3,000 pairs of six seabird species nest. It is one of the largest known breeding colonies of glaucous-winged gulls on the B.C. coast—more than 2,000 pairs. Other nesting species here, in descending order of abundance, are pelagic cormorant, double-crested cormorant, pigeon guillemot, black oystercatcher and tufted puffin. The puffin, a rarity this far south, is represented on Mandarte by only one or two pairs. The Victoria Natural History Society charters a boat for a visit to Mandarte each July.

Mitlenatch Island in the Strait of Georgia off Campbell River is a nature park and has park naturalists on duty there during the summer. It has nesting glaucous-winged gulls, pelagic cormorants, pigeon guillemots and black oystercatchers, but it is also a good spot to see summering nonbreeding birds of several other species.

Another nesting island is Cleland Island near Tofino off Vancouver Island's outer coast. Cleland has nesting glaucous-winged gulls, pigeon guillemots, fork-tailed and Leach's petrels, rhinoceros auklets and tufted puffins. Park naturalist Wayne Campbell has counted 4,000 nesting burrows of Leach's petrels here in one massed 300-by-150-foot colony. Wickaninnish

Beach Park and the tiny islets of Sea-Lion Rocks are about 20 miles from Cleland. Sea-Lion Rocks have the only known breeding colony of Brandt's cormorants in Canada; they are also favourite hauling-out grounds of sea lions.

Boats can usually be chartered for summer visits to all these bird islands, but visitors should not plan on going ashore near the colonies during nesting times. The birds can be adequately and often better seen when cruising offshore. Disturbances that force flocks of alarmed birds to leave their nests result in egg breakage and chilling, frightened nestlings fall from cliffs or run away and never find their parents again, but the major harm is that eggs and young are left exposed to predation by crows.

Crows are always lingering on the fringes of seabird colonies, waiting for opportunities to snatch eggs or nestlings when parents leave them unprotected. A common practice is for two crows to team up. One will harass a nestling gull or cormorant by divebombing it until the bird finally becomes exasperated and leaps up at the teasing crow. Meanwhile the second crow has been waiting just outside the range of the nesting bird's bill, and when the angered gull or cormorant rises momentarily off its nest, the crow dashes in and punctures one of the eggs. Usually, when the gull or cormorant sees the broken egg, it abandons the nest immediately, and the victorious crows move in to feast. If the eggs are difficult to open because they are in an advanced state of incubation and contain well developed embryos, the astute crow flies up with an egg and drops it on a rock to break it.

When humans frighten entire flocks of seabirds off their nests all at once, the resultant plundering by crows can wipe out in minutes most of the whole season's reproduction. The crows are shrewd nest robbers, flying from a couple of miles away when they see a boat approaching a seabird colony, for they know that boats and people often flush birds and produce a banquet of unprotected eggs and young.

Of the remote, northern seabird colonies, the most exciting and biggest by far is uninhabited Triangle Island, the outermost of the Scott Islands which are scattered like broken beads for

The Pacific coast's rocky shoreline provides many excellent nesting sites for sea birds. The map at right gives the location of the famous sea bird colonies described fully in the accompanying text.

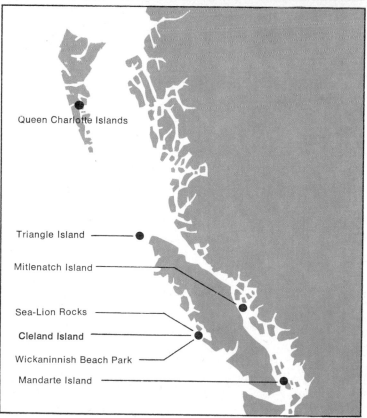

Queen Charlotte Islands

Triangle Island

Mitlenatch Island

Sea-Lion Rocks

Cleland Island

Wickaninnish Beach Park

Mandarte Island

30 miles off the northern tip of Vancouver Island. Slightly less than a mile across, the island has rock cliffs that rise steeply several hundred feet out of the battering sea or above narrow, boulder-strewn strips of beach. But many of the cliffs have a stairway-like profile, their sheer rock faces grading into steep slopes in places where soil has accumulated and grass and bushes grow. The upper main section of the island consists of hilly meadows of grass or tangles of dwarfed salmonberry and salal; there are no trees. Thus Triangle has a variety of nesting habitats which makes it the best example of a seabird apartment on Canada's Pacific coast. Of a possible 15 Pacific coast seabirds and seabird-associates, 13 nest on Triangle. Since several are burrow nesters that come in from the sea only at night, it is impossible to make more than a rough estimate of numbers, but the island's nesting population is tens of thousands.

Occupying the "ground floor" of a typical nesting cliff on Triangle Island are black oystercatchers which lay their eggs in hollows on gravelly beaches usually just above high-tide mark. On the "second floor"–the talus of heaped boulders and stone fragments which lie at the foot of every rock cliff–are pigeon guillemots; their nests, lined only with a few stones or shell fragments, are usually hidden in natural crannies under or among the rocks.

On ledges of the precipitous cliffs which rear up from the beaches and talus are the murres and pelagic cormorants, highly social birds that nest in dense hordes, the murres almost shoulder to shoulder, the cormorants spread out a little more thinly.

Triangle Island has about 1,500 pairs of nesting murres– their only known breeding colony on Canada's Pacific. They build no nests and each pair has only a single egg. Incubating birds stand upright, holding the egg on top of their feet against the unfeathered brood-patch of the abdomen. The eggs are sharply tapered or pear-shaped so that they roll in a tight circle, which reduces the danger of their falling off the narrow nesting ledges. The cliff shelves are covered so densely with eggs or downy chicks that ornithologists have often wondered how a murre recognizes its own when it returns from a feeding flight at sea, but observations of banded birds have shown that the same pair always returns to the same egg or young.

Murres and cormorants are large birds and their size provides them with some protection against marauding crows and peregrine falcons, therefore they are able to nest on the open cliff faces. Five other seabird species on Triangle Island are smaller and they survive by digging burrows as hiding places for their nests. These burrow nesters are the tufted puffin, Cassin's and rhinoceros auklets, and Leach's and fork-tailed petrels. Though all need turf or sand for nest-hole burrowing, each species has its special requirements and a place of its own which sort them out into separate nesting communities.

Triangle's perpendicular rock cliffs are broken at various levels by slopes growing with grass, and occasionally with bushes. The tufted puffins prefer the lowermost of these grass slopes, perhaps because puffins fly more easily from land and do not require as much height to get airborne as the auklets and petrels. Cassin's auklets use similar, open grassy slopes at higher levels. Rhinoceros auklets shun the bare, grassy areas and nest only where there are thick tangles of bushes to cushion their clumsy landings and hide their nesting burrows. There are more of all three of these species nesting on Triangle Island than anywhere else on British Columbia's coast. The uppermost, "penthouse floor"–the smoother grass slopes and meadows of the island's top–is the domain of the petrels.

This ecological separation into non-conflicting communities is true not just of nesting sites within a colony, but also of the manner and places in which each species hunts and feeds at sea. Each one harvests a different food crop.

The oystercatcher, a shorebird, feeds along the edge of the sea on the intertidal life of the rocks and sand.

The pigeon guillemot, a diver, catches small fish in shallow water near shore. Guillemots fly back and forth throughout the day, bringing one fish at a time to their young.

Murres and cormorants, larger birds capable of deep diving and rapid underwater swimming, hunt in deeper water offshore and catch larger fish. They feed their young throughout the day, the murres bringing in one fish at a time, the cormorants by regurgitating partially digested fish. A cormorant chick, when feeding, thrusts its bill and sometimes its whole head down the parent's throat.

A tufted puffin, one of the most attractive birds on the Pacific coast, strikes a comic pose with his beak full of fish.

BIRD
COLONIES

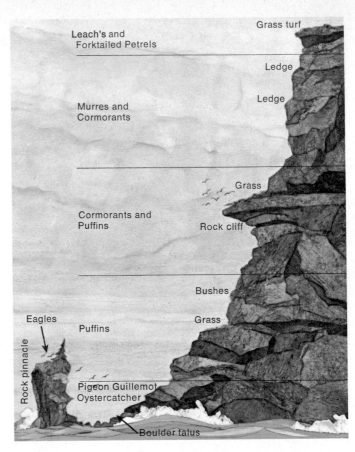

Grass turf

Leach's and
Forktailed Petrels

Ledge

Ledge

Murres and
Cormorants

Grass

Cormorants and
Puffins

Rock cliff

Bushes

Eagles

Puffins

Grass

Rock pinnacle

Pigeon Guillemot
Oystercatcher

Boulder talus

High-rise — the natural solution

A nesting colony along the coast is filled with various
bird species, each seeking its particular nesting
environment. The oystercatchers at the base of the cliff
seek to be near their food supply; the cormorants
prefer rocky ledges, puffins seek grassy slopes, while
eagles prefer rock pinnacles.

◄ *Double crested cormorants
and pelagic cormorants
nest on Mandarte Island.*

Two glaucous-winged gulls ►
*fight for living space on
an overcrowded bird colony.*

Mew gull young wait patiently for the return of the adult birds.

Voracious nestlings of the northwestern crow will mature rapidy into adult birds.

A black oystercatcher surveys the rocky beach on which it nests.

A blue heron stands quietly on its long legs until an unwary fish swims within range of its lightning fast beak.

Puffins are also diurnal, deep-water feeders that operate well offshore, but they utilize small fish and thus do not compete with murres and cormorants. They fly to their nest burrows with beakfulls of as many as eight fish held crosswise in their huge bills, the fish tails flashing in the sun. The manner in which a puffin manages to hold onto half a dozen wriggling fish when it opens its bill to capture a seventh or eighth one is one of nature's tantalizing mysteries. It is believed it may hold the previously caught fish against its upper mandible with its tongue.

The auklets and petrels are mainly nocturnal around their nesting colonies, spending the days far out at sea, returning to their nests to relieve mates or to feed young only at night–usually just after dusk or just before dawn. But even these foragers of the distant reaches of the sea have their own non-competitive feeding domains, for the auklets are divers and underwater hunters, and the petrels are surface feeders. Rhinoceros auklets catch small fish, Cassin's auklets tiny shrimps and plankton animals. Petrels feed on still smaller plankton organisms gleaned from the ocean's surface.

Auklet feeding flights have been calculated to take them 60 miles or more from their nests. Rhinoceros auklets are sometimes seen off Victoria carrying fish toward nesting colonies, the nearest of which are 30 miles to the south on the Washington coast. But it is believed that auklet mates exchange nesting duties every night, and the jabbering calls of greeting and the whirring of wings in the darkness as vast flocks of the "swing shift" come in from the sea turn the colonies into bedlams of sound.

Petrels are even more distant fliers, their feeding flights taking them several hundred miles out to sea–so far that birds in the nesting burrows maintain lonely vigils without food for as long as six days before mates return to spell them off. Petrel colonies like those on Triangle Island are so silent and inactive during the day that one can be standing where thousands of birds are hidden in burrows beneath one's feet without realizing it, because the burrow entrances are small and obscured by vegetation. But when darkness settles, the colonies suddenly come alive with the fluttering, ghost-like forms of returning petrels and their eerie, twittering calls.

The distance between petrel feeding grounds at sea and the nesting colonies is so great that petrels cannot feed fresh food to their young. Instead the returning parent feeds the single young bird by ejecting its oily, evil-smelling stomach contents into the nestling's throat. Young petrels wait so long between feedings that they are among the slowest growing birds, spending 10 weeks in the nest before the parents finally abandon them. Then the young emerge from the burrows and take off alone on their first tumbling flights down the cliffs to the sea.

Three non-seabirds whose ways of life are inextricably linked with the big seabird colonies are crows, peregrine falcons and bald eagles.

Peregrines in most parts of the world are bird hunters that kill a variety of birds, but the Pacific peregrine population is a distinctive and highly specialized one. They nest only in seabird colonies and live almost entirely on either the ancient murrelet or Cassin's auklet. Usually about four pairs nest among the seabirds of Triangle Island, the eyries high on cliff ledges from which the peregrines can swoop down on the massed flights of seabirds that are streaming in every dusk and dawn. There are no ancient murrelets on Triangle; murres, cormorants, rhinoceros auklets and puffins are too large for peregrines to carry back to their nests; pigeon guillemots are loners and thus more difficult to capture, and the petrels are night flyers; therefore Triangle's peregrines concentrate on Cassin's auklets and catch little else.

The world's fastest-flying bird, the peregrine swoops down on its prey in dives that have been clocked at 180 miles per hour, and it has been known to pass light airplanes in flight. Swift, adroit, highly manoeuvrable in the air, it dives onto its auklet prey, raking it with its talons, loosing a cloud of feathers, usually striking such a powerful blow that the auklet is killed instantly in midair. The peregrine then loops back, catching the falling auklet before it can drop to the ground or sea.

Eagles are attracted to seabird colonies by the bodies of dead seabirds that normal mortality among the thousands of birds always ensures. Around colonies like those of Triangle Island, where there are no trees, the eagles nest on the tops of rock pinnacles that rise out of the sea in great columns 200 to 300 feet high. At least a dozen eagles nest on Triangle and its neighbouring islets. They are cunning spongers and often let other birds do their food hunting. They sit patiently watching crows searching through seaweed tangles at low tide, and when they see that a crow has found a large fish they swoop down and steal the fish from the crow. They even steal from the swift and powerful peregrine falcon. When peregrine eggs hatch, the parent falcon begins killing more auklets than they can use, and stockpile them near the eyries to feed later to the nestlings. Eagles frequently raid these peregrine stockpiles, and during this period the eagles too are living mainly on Cassin's auklets.

Only two Pacific coast seabirds are missing from Triangle Island's nesting colonies. The first is the ancient murrelet, another burrow nester, that breeds around the Asian and Alaskan north Pacific, but southward only as far as the Queen Charlottes. The other is the marbled murrelet, extremely common at many points along the Pacific coast, yet its nesting habits are still a secret that only those thousands of marbled murrelets know–the biggest, most frustrating mystery that remains in North American ornithology.

---

16 THE MURRELET MYSTERY

The nest of the marbled murrelet has been sought by ornithologists and naturalists for a century. It is probably the most common of the alcid group of seabirds, occurring in flocks of hundreds at many spots along the B.C. coast. It is obviously a common nester in innumerable places; eggs have been taken from the oviducts of shot females, young murrelets still unable to fly frequently indicate the nests must be near, and there are numerous observations of adults carrying food, obviously to feed nestlings. But the nest itself and where it is located is still unknown.

It is incredible, one is tempted to say absurd, that an authenticated nest of this abundant bird has yet to be found.

The marbled murrelet is a small, robin-sized, chubby, neckless seabird, a rather nondescript dark brown in its summer breeding dress, but patterned with black and white in winter. It occurs from central California to Alaska and down the Asian coast to Japan. It is especially abundant around the shores of Vancouver Island and the Queen Charlottes.

There is a long list of clues, including several contradictory claims of nest and egg discoveries. But in every case the reports have reached ornithologists second- or third-hand, too late to be checked, and lacking proof of accurate identification.

In June, 1953, Walter Feyer, a birdwatcher at Masset in the Queen Charlottes, felled a large hemlock and in the debris of broken limbs picked up a stunned adult murrelet and fragments of egg shells. The bird and shells were confirmed by a biologist to be a marbled murrelet. But Feyer's search turned up no nest, therefore the discovery does not reveal whether the nest was in the tree, on the ground in the path of its fall, or in an underground burrow which was ploughed open by the impact of the falling tree.

Another similar occurrence was reported from Holberg, northern Vancouver Island, in 1967, where loggers felled a cedar and two young birds were reported to have "fallen out of the tree." R. D. Harris, a Canadian Wildlife Service biologist at Vancouver, verified that they were young marbled murrelets, fully fledged, and would have flown in about a week. But as in Feyer's discovery, it was impossible to determine whether the nest was in a tree cavity, on one of its branches, on the ground, or in an uprooted burrow.

There is a report that a Russian ornithologist found a nest in Siberia, eight miles inland from the Sea of Okhotsk, in 1961. This nest was described as a natural cushion of lichen on a tree branch eight feet above the ground, but further details are scant. If marbled murrelets of the North American coast nest in this open manner on tree branches, it is incredible that after a century of logging during which thousands of square miles of coastal forest have been denuded that no nest of such a common bird has been found.

One of the most preposterous features of the mystery is that every June and July flocks of several hundred marbled murrelets can be seen in waters around Saanich Peninsula within ten miles of Victoria, and they obviously nest somewhere near. Allen Poynter, a Victoria naturalist, and many others have studied these flocks intensely for several years. In late June and early July when they are apparently feeding young, the murrelets assemble in rafts offshore every evening, each bird holding one to three small fish in its bill. But they always wait until the minutes between dusk and darkness before they take off and fly inland toward the spots where their nests must be. Since they are dark birds flying at 40 to 50 miles per hour, they usually disappear in a few seconds against the towering, night-shadowed backdrop of mountains and forests. Poynter has mapped their inland flights at several points, all within 20 miles of Victoria, and he has scoured the mountainsides and forest in their flight paths for nesting clues, to no avail. Poynter's searches usually end abruptly, for one day during the first week in July the flocks on the open water will suddenly include large numbers of noisy, excited young murrelets that have flown down to the sea from their nests during darkness the night before, indicating that the mysterious nesting is over and the marbled murrelet's secret is safe for another year.

Charles Guiguet, ornithologist at the provincial museum, Victoria, has combed the B.C. coast from Washington to Alaska for 35 years and has amassed an impressive array of murrelet breeding clues, but no clinching proof of a nest. Countless times he has shown marbled murrelet skins to Haida Indians who take large numbers of birds and eggs from the Queen Charlotte seabird colonies for food and know the seabird ways better than any white man. But each time when Guiguet asks "Where does she lay her eggs?" the Indian response is invariably a shrug and a murmured "Nobody know."

Guiguet doubts that the marbled murrelet is a burrow nester because the plumage of alcids that nest in burrows has a distinctive, musty odour from the long periods spent underground, and the marbled murrelet does not have this odour.

The two cases in which eggs or young turned up when trees were felled suggest nesting in forest, but these may have been abnormal nesting locations, because only twice in a century of logging has tree-felling produced such nesting evidence. It has been suggested that they nest in salal, the widespread coastal shrub that produces thickets so impenetrable a man cannot walk through them. But the rhinoceros auklet and ancient murrelet, both of them less abundant birds, nest in such bushy thickets and their nests are frequently found.

There is also the mountaintop theory—that they nest high up on peaks, perhaps among snowfields, perhaps in the niches of sheer cliff and chasm faces. The nesting story of Kittlitz's murrelet gives credence to the mountaintop theory. Kittlitz's murrelet nests were also unknown for a long time, and when finally discovered they were found to be on rock outcrops amid snowfields high above timberline. Yet nests of Kittlitz's murrelet did

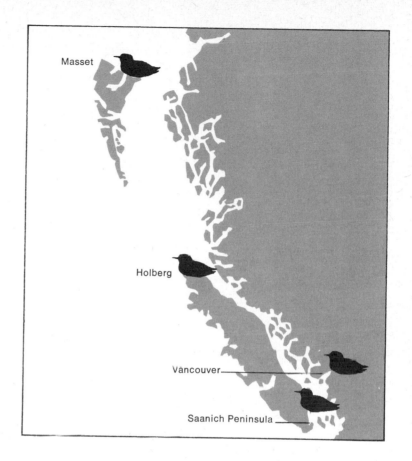

Although its nest has never been discovered, the marbled murrelet can be seen in large numbers at each of the places noted on the map.

125

turn up eventually, despite the fact they are on remote mountain peaks that are climbed much less than the southern peaks in the marbled murrelet's breeding range.

One possibility–a far-out one–remains. Marbled murrelets are sometimes seen on inland lakes. Could they nest in burrows like those of muskrats and beaver which have their entrances underwater? For a diving bird, such an underwater burrow sloping upward to a nesting chamber above water level is at least biologically possible. But if the marbled murrelet nests in this manner, it is the only bird to have discovered such a cunning nest-hiding trick.

So the puzzle remains. Meanwhile, thousands of marbled murrelets take off from the sea every summer evening and disappear into the darkness inland. Somewhere at the end of those countless evening flights lies the answer to the last big North American bird mystery.

17 TWO FAMOUS ALIENS

Among the Pacific coast's 200-odd strictly land birds there are two species with unusual stories. Both are aliens imported originally by immigrants as nostalgic reminders of the homelands they left.

They are the skylark, exalted by generations of English poets, and the crested mynah, a doughty Asian. Their special status stems from the fact that they can be seen nowhere else in North America except in the Victoria and Vancouver vicinities.

Thousands of Old World birds of numerous species were brought to North America and released by homesick pioneers, a once-popular practice that is illegal throughout the continent today. Almost all of these introductions failed, although two– the house sparrow and European starling–were spectacularly successful. Among a half-dozen or so other introductions that have had local successes, the most notable are British Columbia's skylarks and crested mynahs.

The skylark's natural range is across temperate Eurasia from Britain to Japan. Many early British settlers tried to establish it in various places in North America. Among the many importations were 200 birds released near Victoria in 1903 and another 49 in 1913. These are the only North American skylark imports whose descendants have survived.

The skylark, a field dweller, became acclimatized and well established throughout the farming country of Saanich Peninsula that extends about 15 miles north of Victoria. The colony today consists of around 1,000 birds, mainly in the weedy fields along Martindale Road, about midway up the east side of Saanich Peninsula. The skylarks occupy all the suitable open country in the region and their habitat is now shrinking because of Victoria's suburban expansion. As this expansion continues, it is inevitable that skylark numbers will be reduced.

How was the skylark able to gain this foothold on southern Vancouver Island but nowhere else on the continent?

A major reason is probably climate. This is the dry-inner coast climatic zone of mild, almost snowless winters that is very similar to the climate of the British Isles from which the skylark imports came. Skylarks are ground feeders and cannot survive where the ground is covered with snow more than a few weeks a year. So the skylarks found a climate here, like that of their ancestral home. But other factors also undoubtedly contributed to their colonizing success.

Saanich Peninsula was originally forest, and the fields the skylarks inhabited were a man-made environment. At the time the skylarks arrived, these fields were relatively new and probably not yet fully colonized by native field birds, therefore the skylarks were able to move into a newly-created habitat without encountering severe competition from other birds.

Finally, and possibly of great significance, is the fact that the skylarks brought to Vancouver Island happened to be members of a non-migratory population. In the Old World some skylarks migrate south for the winter and some do not. If Victoria's skylarks had carried with them a migratory instinct which goaded them into flying southward in autumn, the hazards of such a migration in a new, unknown land would probably have wiped them out. But apparently the initial birds were trapped in Britain during winter and were thus non-migratory, so when they were released on Vancouver Island there was no inbred migration urge to force them out of what is possibly the only region in North America where they could survive.

The mynahs are starlings, several species of which are native to India and the Far East, and like their relative, the

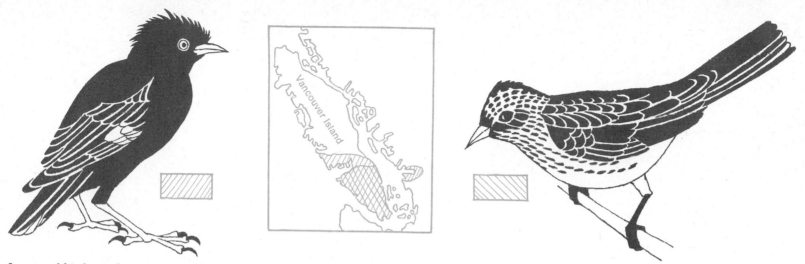

Imported birds — the crested mynahs (left) and skylark (right) were brought to the Pacific coast by early settlers. The skylark reminded early British settlers of home. It is not known how the mynahs first came to the coast but they have adapted well as the range map shows.

European starling, they are tough, intelligent and adaptive birds that have spread with man's help to many regions of the world. The species that occurs in southern coastal B.C. is the crested mynah, a black, chunky bird somewhat larger than the European starling, with white wing patches and a peculiar bushy crest on its forehead. It has been established in the Vancouver area for 70 years, but unlike the European starling, it has never spread far beyond this original North American beachhead.

It is not known how the first crested mynahs came to Canada, but they reached Vancouver somehow in the 1890's. They may have been brought from China by a Chinese immigrant, or they could have hitch-hiked on a ship from the Orient. One report, unverifiable because its origin is now lost, states that a ship from China was carrying a crate of crested mynahs on its deck for some now-unknown destination; the noisy birds kept the crew awake night after night throughout the voyage, and when the ship reached Vancouver the sleepless, infuriated captain is said to have opened the crate, let the mynahs escape, and he then wired the consignees that their birds had been washed overboard at sea.

The crested mynahs established themselves around Vancouver and spread across the strait to southern Vancouver Island. By 1927 their population reached 20,000 and it was feared that they were about to become a pest throughout the west as the starling then was doing in the east. But the increase was not maintained, their numbers declined, and for many years now the crested mynah population seems to have stabilized at between 2,000 and 3,000.

They are distributed throughout much of Greater Vancouver from Burrard Inlet south to Lulu Island and inland to New Westminster. They are mainly urban birds of streets and backyards. They congregate around buildings in noisy overnight roosts, as the starling also does. The biggest roosts are at Lapointe Pier on Burrard Inlet and Cambie Bridge crossing False Creek. They have now almost disappeared from Vancouver Island, but a few pairs persist at Nanaimo where they are sedentary birds easily found. Just drive to the Simpsons-Sears parking lot and if the bushy-crested birds are not immediately seen on the store roof or on the parking lot picking up dead insects, a brief check of garbage cans in the alleys of the vicinity will usually locate them.

And so, after a hunt for west-coast birds that has taken us to pristine fiords, the misty Queen Charlottes and remote sea cliffs of Triangle and Cleland, we finally end it in a ludicrous search for one of the continent's rarest, amid garbage cans and prowling cats in the back alleys of Nanaimo and Vancouver.

A long-eared owl
ruffles its feathers to
frighten an intruder.

PART FIVE/ CONSERVATION

18 THE HEEDLESS HARVEST

The first European to reach the west coast of Canada and launch its recent era of white man's history was Captain James Cook in 1778. The time that has elapsed since is nothing in the age scale of the mountains, and only one-sixth of the lifetime of a red cedar or Douglas fir. Even by North America's shrunken scale of historical time it is relatively recent, for by 1778 eastern Canada already had flourishing communities and a rapidly expanding population.

So modern man's tenure on the north Pacific shore has been brief. He has been here less than two centuries, in appreciable numbers for less than one century. Yet not since the coming of the Ice Age a million years ago has there been a force that has had such devastating impact on the primeval bounty of forests and wildlife that this coastal land and its waters originally supported.

Captain Cook and his crew found a coast of gigantic forests, pure rivers and teeming life. It has not been an easy coast for resource exploitation, because the rugged terrain has ruled out roads for much of it and there is little agricultural land for self-supporting settlements. As a result, the northern reaches of the coast have a superficial wildness still and many regions of Canada have fared far worse under the blundering, ravaging hand of man. Yet, nevertheless, the despoiling marks of man lie heavy upon it, especially in the south where human population has concentrated.

Today, less than 200 years after Cook's landing, only tiny remnants of the virgin rain forest survive, much of it ravished by logging methods that have prevented or retarded its regrowth. Wildlife has in some instances been aided by man's clearing of forests–deer, for example, have increased as a result of the better browsing provided by shrubby regrowth–but in most cases wildlife has sharply declined, and some species are entirely gone. The fertility of some rivers and coastal waters has been recklessly destroyed by logging, industrial and sewage pollution, their fish population decimated, although some of the great salmon runs still survive as one of the last North American samples of primeval abundance.

It is not my intention to question man's right to tame this coastal wilderness and harvest its natural resources for his own use. But with hindsight now, it is clear that greed and waste, prompted by motives of immediate gain without thought or planning for future yields, produced methods of resource use from which we are reaping steep losses still today. So this and the following chapters will chronicle with shame and sadness the heedless harvest that too often became sheer and wasteful desecration.

It started when Cook's expedition returned to Britain with the exciting news that the Vancouver Island coast had vast numbers of sea otter. This marine mammal with the silky black pelt was already known from Asian shores of the north Pacific as the most valuable fur of the time. The race for the Pacific coast's resources was on, and the sea otter became its first great lure.

It is an unusual animal, five feet long, four times as large as the better known river otter of inland streams and lakes, and it spends its entire life as a swimming mammal of the sea. A dexterous and deep diver, it lives on shellfish garnered from the sea bottom. When resting it floats or swims comically on its back, front legs folded human-like across its chest while it propels itself with webbed, flipper-like hind feet. When it brings a clam or mussel to the surface, it feeds using its chest for a table, often holding a stone on its chest and breaking clam shells by hammering them against it. It sleeps floating on its back in the same manner, sometimes with paws over its eyes to keep out the sun, and when the surf is strong it wraps a ribbon of seaweed kelp around itself to prevent being dashed ashore. Mother otters moor their young with kelp in the same way when they leave on hunting forays–the sea otter version of a playpen.

But the sea otter's Achilles' heel was its unusual fur. Unlike seals and whales which depend for warmth on a thick layer of blubber under the skin, the sea otter obtains its insulation by an unusually soft, velvety fur so fine and dense that it is impregnable to water–the most valuable and exquisite fur of any mammal. Furthermore, since it lives in an environment where there is little seasonal temperature change, the fur is always prime, and the sea otter obtained no relief from hunting pressure as other furbearers do by having a summer season when the hair is shedding.

A few years after Cook's fabulous news reached Britain, the sea otter rush, as profitable and profligate as any gold rush the world has known, was on. Demand soared and the value of a prime otter pelt rose to $4,000 on the London fur market; one cargo might be worth $2 million, and a skipper could retire wealthy on the profits from a single voyage. British, American, Russian and Spanish traders joined in the stampede, and Britain and Spain almost went to war over the control of the lucrative trade out of Vancouver Island and the Queen Charlottes.

The Chinese and Pacific coast Indians had been using sea otter pelts for centuries without seriously reducing the animal's numbers, but now avid and highly organized Europeans turned it into a grisly slaughter. The animals were so tame and trusting that a boat could be rowed among them, and the only weapon needed to kill them was a club. Females were so solicitous of their young that they would not abandon them and a whining pup lifted into a boat would lure its frantic mother to the boat's side where she too could be easily killed. There was no thought of employing a controlled harvest that would ensure a continuing supply.

There were only about 20 years of heavy killing, because sea otters diminished rapidly soon after 1800. Originally they had ranged all around the north Pacific from Japan to California. The record is not clear as to when they became extinct on the coasts of British Columbia, Washington and Oregon, but it was during the mid 1800's, and by late in the century only a small population survived in Alaskan waters; they appeared to be gone everywhere else. Yet the hunt was still going on wherever the animals could be found. The kill was finally outlawed by an international treaty between Canada, U.S., Russia and Japan in 1911, but the protection would probably not have come even then but for the fact that the sea otter at last had become too scarce to support further hunting economically.

In 1938 a small sea otter colony was discovered off Monterey, California, presumably the descendants of a few animals the hunters had missed. But except for this small colony, the sea otter, despite more than half a century of protection, still survives only in Alaska and has not spread out to reoccupy any more of its once-extensive range.

The sea otter, though its story is not widely known, ranks a place in Canadian history equivalent to that of the beaver, for as the beaver lured men into eastern North America, the sea otter drew them to the Pacific. Hundreds of sailors lost their lives in the quest for sea otter fur, but a positive outgrowth of it was the rapid exploring and charting of the Pacific coast. But above all else, the sea otter stands unchallenged as Canadian history's most shameful symbol of man's depraved and infamous disregard for the wealth of wildlife that had occupied this continent for thousands of years before he came. The buffalo and beaver, though reduced to a fragment of their original abundance, were never actually in danger of extinction. The sea otter, on the other hand, was completely exterminated from the Canadian fauna, and it was done purely for economic greed, because unlike the buffalo of the fertile plains, the sea otter occupied a region for which man had no need. Its remote coastal habitat is still there, unchanged, unused by humans, and the sea otter could be there too, because it interfered in no way with the interests of man.

Perhaps before long the sea otter will be back again, because the British Columbia Fish and Wildlife Branch has recently been flying in sea otters livetrapped in Alaska and releasing them off Vancouver Island in an effort to re-establish them.

But two other Pacific coast mammals were pushed full distance down the one-way road to extinction from which they will never return. They were Steller's sea cow and Dawson caribou.

Steller's sea cow was a big, seal-like animal. Females often stood upright in the water exposing prominent breasts and they were one of the sea mammals responsible for sailors' legends about mermaids—perhaps more wishful thinking than conviction, because except for the pendant breasts there was nothing otherwise ladylike about this fat, flippered, bewhiskered swimmer of the sea. The sea cow was first discovered in Bering Strait in 1841; clumsy and defenceless, it was butchered so ruthlessly by whalers for its blubber that all were gone within 27 years. Extinction came so fast that its range and migrations were never accurately known and it is only a guess that it probably at times reached British Columbia waters to rank as a Canadian mammal.

The Dawson caribou is a different story. This stunted, three-foot-high member of the deer family was restricted to a limited range in the boggy northwest corner of the Queen Charlotte Islands where it was so rare that it was seen only a couple of times and never seriously hunted by man. It was probably sinking towards extinction for natural reasons, but man clinched its end by introducing deer to the Queen Charlottes around the turn of the century which became a competitor for the caribou's limited food supply. The last evidence of it were tracks found in 1935. Since then the Queen Charlottes have been combed by loggers and prospectors without further evidence of caribou coming to light, and mammalogists believe it must be extinct today.

This story of wildlife destruction from ignorance, greed and short-sighted opportunism has many more chapters.

The sluicing and sifting of river bars for gold silted rivers removed gravel spawning beds and destroyed salmon runs which, in the years since, would have been worth far more than all the gold obtained. Whalers brought the once-abundant elephant seal, Pacific right whale and grey whale to the verge of extinction; protection in the form of international treaties came in time to save them, but not in time to save Canada's Pacific whaling industry which has virtually ceased because of declining catches. The pilchard, a cousin of the herring that supported a $3 million-a-year fishery until the 1930's, has disappeared, and uncontrolled fishing is believed to have been a major cause.

But the resource exploitation that soon assumed dominance over the pioneer fur, whaling and gold industries was lumbering. It is still the mainstay of British Columbia's economy, producing almost 50 cents of every dollar earned, but despite this, in the revealing perspective of historical hindsight it becomes another story of heedless harvest.

19 OF LOGS AND LADY'S SLIPPERS

When steam power replaced horses around 1900 and made large scale logging possible, the coastal forests were attacked with the same heedless disregard for the future that had marked the plunder of sea otters and whales. The biggest, most valuable trees grew along the coast, where cheap removal of logs by rafting on inlets and the sea offered the biggest profits; so the coastal forests took the brunt of the carnage, as they still do today.

Lumbering's contempt for future needs took two forms. First, it swept almost all the biggest and finest trees before it, leaving practically none readily accessible to the public in parks or wilderness preserves that could serve as living museums of the forest grandeur that is now all but gone. A few more Cathedral Groves handy to Vancouver and Victoria would have far more value today, aesthetically, educationally and as earners of tourist revenue, than they yielded originally as sawlogs. Secondly, until recent years, logging was done with little recognition that there would be other generations who would need future forest crops from the same land.

The most profitable logging method—and therefore the method inevitably followed—was clear-cutting in which everything was flattened, and then anything not worth hauling out was left on the ground to become a tinder box that was usually swept within a few years by fires. There was no thought of replanting, leaving seed trees, or protecting soil and streams against erosion to encourage natural regrowth. Fires had always been a normal though infrequent feature of the coastal forest ecology, but now a new, unnatural, highly destructive type of ground-hugging fire resulted from the loggers' slash—fires that concentrated their heat onto the ground beneath instead of dissipating it into the crowns of standing trees high above—and they were allowed to burn out the humus of soils that had been thousands of years accumulating. Because of the coast's heavy rainfall, the thin soils of steep hillsides and ridges, bared now by clear-cutting and the ground-slash fires, were swept away.

The legacy of this wanton profit-taking is hundreds of thousands of acres either barren of forests today, or grown up in scrub forests of alder and maple where valuable Douglas fir could be growing if it had been given a chance. Up to 50 years of growth has already been lost from what were originally some of the most productive forest sites. Foresters estimate that if errors and abuses of the past could be corrected, modern scientific forest management applied, and every acre returned to its virgin rate of production, the coast forests could be producing three times their current wood yield.

Since the beginning of British Columbia's logging history, the coast forest, rich and easily logged, has been used as a quick cash return to finance the opening up of less profitable and more remote forest regions of the interior. This policy is still being

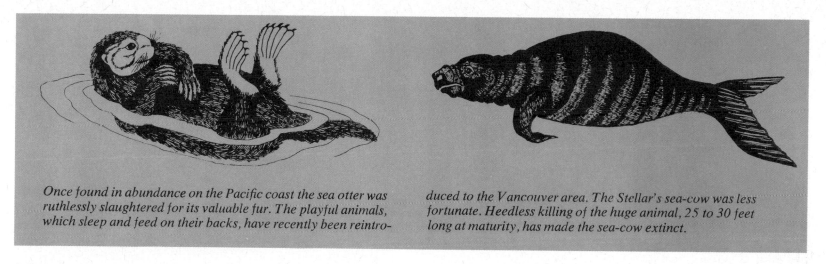

Once found in abundance on the Pacific coast the sea otter was ruthlessly slaughtered for its valuable fur. The playful animals, which sleep and feed on their backs, have recently been reintro-duced to the Vancouver area. The Stellar's sea-cow was less fortunate. Heedless killing of the huge animal, 25 to 30 feet long at maturity, has made the sea-cow extinct.

followed. For permanent yield, annual forest cut must be balanced by annual regrowth. The rate of regrowth is difficult to assess for large regions, but it is believed that annual cut in the coast forests, especially the cut of Douglas fir, its most valuable tree, is still almost three times greater than annual regrowth. On the other hand, annual cut in interior forests, where the difficulties are greater and profits less, is only half the annual growth. The British Columbia Forest Service is striving to shift logging pressure from the coast to the interior, but patterns of forest use established in the carefree days when forests were believed inexhaustible are now deeply imbedded in the province's industrial complex. They will take years to adjust and change.

British Columbia's other big resource-based industry, its commercial fisheries, is a brighter story. The fish resource also went through an early history of abuse and decline, but the fishery had a built-in potential for rapid recovery that forests lacked—a salmon matures in four years, whereas a Douglas fir requires a couple of centuries. The pilchard has disappeared, but most other fish of commercial value have recovered under management and controls.

The most important are the five species of salmon, which are unique in that they mature at sea where they convert the great food wealth of the ocean into a food source prized by man, but they are entirely dependent on freshwater lakes and rivers for spawning grounds. Thus they are peculiarly vulner-

able to anything that deteriorates or blocks their spawning rivers, such as flooding, silting, damming or pollution. The most important salmon producer of Canada's Pacific coast is the Fraser River, probably the greatest salmon-producing river of the world. Its production plunged following needless blocking of the river in 1913 when railway builders dumped millions of tons of rock into the canyon at Hell's Gate. In the Columbia River of Washington state, another big salmon breeder, a spate of dams for irrigation, logging and hydro-electric production cut the salmon yield to 15 percent of its original level, from which it will never recover. So Canada's fishery managers had these two vivid proofs that the valuable salmon industry could be wiped out by river destruction more quickly than by overfishing at sea. As a result, Canada's salmon production has been carefully nurtured and the catches controlled for many years. Salmon yields are almost back to their original peaks, a heartening example of what cooperating with nature can accomplish.

But new threats, especially on the Fraser, loom ahead. Salmon are especially vulnerable to river-mouth pollution when they are making the hazardous adjustment to freshwater after several years spent in saltwater at sea. Vancouver, with new sewage treatment plants, is no longer the serious polluter of the lower Fraser that it was, but growing towns upriver continue to pour raw sewage and industrial wastes into it. A still greater threat is the Fraser's hydro-electric potential. Development of the Fraser for power production would inevitably wipe out its

The harvest of the sea — salmon, found in abundance on the coast, are caught by the thousands each year.

salmon run, as occurred in the Columbia. It is estimated that power from a fully harnessed Fraser would be worth $400 million a year, whereas its salmon production is worth $50 to $60 million annually. But weighing the conflicting values is not that simple. With cheap and abundant nuclear power promising to replace hydro-electric power, the Fraser's electricity might be needed for only a matter of decades. Meanwhile, a protein-hungry world will have a growing need for the Fraser's great production of salmon. Protein shortage, not power shortage, looms as the impending crisis of the future, and to trade the Fraser's salmon for its hydro-electric power might in half a century turn out to have been a poor bargain.

But at least up to now, because of the huge industry they support, the salmon have been left with the river habitats they need for reproduction. However, some other forms of wildlife that lack the obvious economic value of the salmon are not faring as well. We are no longer slaughtering wildlife to the point of extinction as we did with the sea otter, but we may be producing the same result, indirectly but just as devastatingly, by destroying the living space that wildlife must have to survive. The most flagrant current example is Vancouver's new industrial harbour, and residential expansion southward across the Fraser delta region which is gobbling up the west coast's most important waterfowl wintering ground.

Feeding and nesting areas during migration and over-wintering periods are as essential for waterfowl survival as nesting grounds. The Pacific coast is one of the continent's most important waterfowl flyways, but its steep, mountainous nature provides very few of the shallow, muddy foreshores that most species of ducks and geese require for feeding. There are some waterfowl wintering grounds around southern Vancouver Island, but the biggest and most important by far are the vast stretches of tidal mudflats and marshes that snake for 40 miles south of Vancouver around the U.S. enclave of Point Roberts into Boundary Bay. Here, for thousands of years, great flocks of ducks and geese have been resting and feeding during migration or staying for the winter.

It is probably the largest waterfowl haven in Canada. Ducks and geese funnel into the area from nesting grounds in the prairies, Alaska, even distant reaches of Siberia. It is used by millions of birds each year as successive flocks pass through on migration, finding here the refuge, rest and food they need to complete their journeys. Hundreds of thousands fly no farther, and make this their winter home. More than 100,000 ducks have been counted on Boundary Bay alone in a single day. Each April, flocks of tens of thousands of black brant, found only on the Pacific coast, make it their main resting stop on the long flight between Mexico and the Arctic. At times, sections of foreshore are whitened with snow geese, and Russian leg bands indicate that many of them come from nesting grounds on Siberia's Wrangel Island far out in the Arctic Ocean.

Major sections of this shoreline are now being transformed into a sprawling complex of deep-sea harbour, bulk-loading installations, railway right-of-ways and storage yards for Vancouver's booming marine expansion. Conservationists, hunters, parks and recreational authorities have tried vainly to steer Vancouver's growth elsewhere, stressing that not just waterfowl habitat is being lost, but also rich agricultural land and beaches of priceless value for an area already lamentably poor in parks and recreational space. But in the value scales of our age, there is no other way.

Waterfowl are slow to change their instinctively-fixed migratory routes and stopovers. In this case, because of the rugged, deepwater coast elsewhere, there may be no alternative wintering grounds available to them. Of all the wildlife habitat changes that man has wrought on the Pacific coast, this destruction of the Fraser delta foreshore may prove to be the most damaging of them all.

Its great flocks of ducks and geese, stringing like beads across the sky, pitching down with thundering wings to the tidal shallows, have been a distinctive, character-defining feature of this coastal land, like surf, Douglas fir and the red flashes of spawning salmon, since the melting ice bared it to rain and sun 11,000 years ago. Vancouver may boom into one of the world's superports, a smoggy, derrick-spiked replica of many others like it, but the gatherings of waterfowl that once made it unique will be gone.

At least the waterfowl, conspicuous and recognizable, will be missed. But there are other vanishing species, and only naturalists know them as irreplaceable links in the natural mosaic and note their passing with nostalgia and regret. This is especially true of some plants and trees that grow in Canada only as precarious beachheads in the unique climatic zone of southern Vancouver Island and the lower mainland. Here urban development, trampling, picking and forest clearing have tipped the slender balances of survival and are slowly exterminating them from the Canadian scene. The mountain lady's slipper, a large and showy orchid, survives in a few places on the mainland but has disappeared from Vancouver Island. The prickly pear cactus, easily wiped out by trampling, now survives around Victoria only in Beacon Hill Park, Gordon Head and on some of the little-frequented Gulf Islands. The Garry oak, B.C.'s only oak, also restricted to a limited range around Victoria, is threatened by the city's expansion and before long may remain only in a few parks.

So this is the record of less than two centuries of man's occupation. Only the rugged, granite mountains have remained unaffected—the one element of the natural scene too obdurate and impregnable for man to despoil and change.

20 PARKS AND THE NEW RESOURCE

A new, burgeoning, resource-based industry, the potential of which was undreamed of two decades ago, is creating a revolution in resource evaluations. It is recreation and travel. The resource on which it depends is simply scenery and relatively undisturbed outdoor space. It is unique in that it uses its resource without destroying it. In certain circumstances it is making traditional concepts of resource exploitation uneconomic; a towering stand of Douglas fir, for example, no longer has to be cut to turn it into dollars—in the right place, it might be worth more left standing just to be looked at. A revolution indeed.

At its current rate of annual increase, tourist traffic in ten years will be the second largest British Columbia resource-based industry, exceeded only by forestry. But attempts like this to attach a cash value to recreational assets consistently undervalue them. Recreation experts say the main value lies in more abstract areas, such as relaxation, mental and physical health, and the labour stability and productivity these induce. The fact that it also brings in outside revenue, they say, is a fortunate and lucrative byproduct.

A portion of British Columbia's travel revenue, of course, results from urban attractions; but the biggest, though unmeasurable, part of its outdoor attraction is the land itself. The main system of packaging by which scenery and undisturbed nature are made available to the public and preserved as investments for the future are parks.

The hinterlands of the province have an enormous potential for outdoor recreation that has yet hardly been tapped. But there is already a grave shortage of parks and recreational space in and around Greater Vancouver, the province's main population centre, where it is most needed for short-term, evening, after-work and weekend use.

Vancouver, for all its superb natural beauty and the recreational assets of its setting, is a glaring example of unimaginative planning for future recreation needs. Stanley Park, in its heart, is one of the finest city parks on the continent, and Garibaldi Provincial Park, 50 miles away, is a splendid mountain playground containing large wilderness areas; but in the years since these early park provisions were made, Vancouver has been allowed to expand willy-nilly with little attempt to add to its park system to keep pace with population needs. The Fraser delta and Boundary Bay region south of the city is rapidly slipping away. Currently accepted standards of park needs are 64 acres per thousand of population (which is expected to increase to 94 acres per thousand by the year 2 000 because of increasing leisure, wealth and mobility), and by these standards the Vancouver area has only about half the park space it should have. The Lower Mainland Regional Planning Board has said that a program to set up adequate park space would cost the equivalent of one movie ticket per person per year. But each year Vancouver's park shortage grows more acute.

There are many categories of parks. Vancouver needs small parks for single-day use of local residents. For long-term vacation use and tourist lures, the need is for big, remote, wilderness parks—the big guns of a park system which only national and provincial governments can provide. National and provincial parks have important roles in wildlife and water conservation, but their main purpose is to preserve regions with outstanding natural attractions as wilderness playgrounds and living museums of the primeval land. To fill these roles, one need is paramount—they must be retained in or near virgin condition,

AN OUTDOOR CLASSROOM

Campers at Long Beach, many of them children, investigate a large skate stranded by the falling tide. Familiarity with nature will hopefully create a generation that will prevent the needless destruction of our natural resources like the small bird (above) killed by oil pollution along the coast.

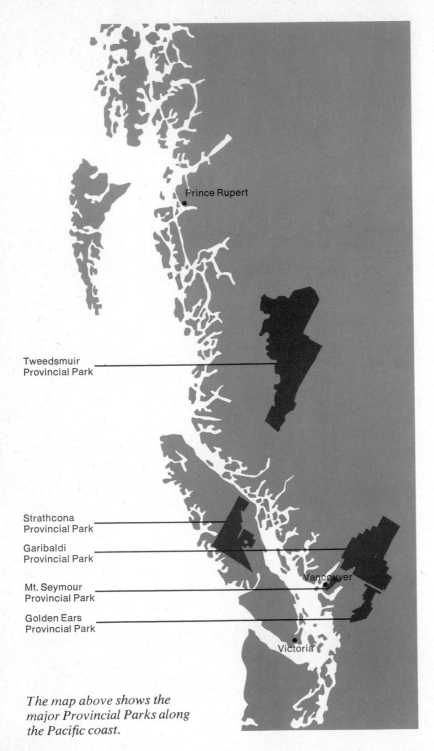

Tweedsmuir
Provincial Park

Strathcona
Provincial Park

Garibaldi
Provincial Park

Mt. Seymour
Provincial Park

Golden Ears
Provincial Park

Prince Rupert

Vancouver

Victoria

The map above shows the major Provincial Parks along the Pacific coast.

industrial and resource exploitation rigidly excluded, and development restricted to the limited roads, campgrounds and overnight accommodation required to make them accessible for types of outdoor recreation in keeping with their aims.

The big wilderness parks must be set aside in undeveloped regions before settlement and industrial development reach them and destroy their primeval nature. It is a simple matter to draw a line on a map around some hinterland region and say that's going to be a park, but as pressures for resource use like logging and mining develop in the future, it becomes increasingly difficult for a government to resist the tough and persistent commercial lobbying and keep the resource developers out.

British Columbia's record of large wilderness park preservation has been a mixed and contradictory story of good intentions, wise early provision of park space, but a weak and lamentable reluctance to take a firm stand on preservation when commercial pressures start gnawing at the park borders.

It is a young land politically and economically, still a frontier land in many respects, imbued with the eager, pioneering zeal of such lands to conquer its wildernesses, tap its yet-unreached resources and expand its industrial base. Except around Vancouver, it has not yet seriously felt the pinch of disappearing recreational space, as Ontario and many parts of the U.S. have. So, when the chips are down, and a park's preservation comes in conflict with an opportunity to cash in on a natural resource, often the preservation policies and promises are shunted aside in a grab for new resource dollars.

British Columbia has an active and imaginative Parks Branch of qualified and able people, and an excellent, growing network of small roadside parks and campgrounds. Some of the development of its smaller parks, especially nature museums and nature interpretation programs, is as good as any on the continent. But when it comes to guarding the big parks, the higher echelons of government do not share the Parks Branch's enthusiasm and dedication.

Fifteen years ago British Columbia had a provincial parks system on paper that included a number of large samples of primitive country. But the legal basis for park preservation in B.C. is riddled with loopholes. Parks can be wiped out, their boundaries changed or their degree of protection altered by cabinet closed-door orders-in-council, without reference to the legislature, and without the knowledge of the public until it is too late for public reaction to change the decisions. The Department of Mines has been left in full control of the province's minerals, including those within parks; Lands, Forests and Water Resources control all waters, in parks or out; the Department of Highways is a law to itself when it comes to highway construction and can ignore park boundaries. Thus the Parks Branch is peculiarly emasculated by a hierarchy of liege lords over its head who have prior claim to some of the parks' most essential recreational assets.

Governments have repeatedly taken advantage of this weak legislation to throw parks open to industrial encroachments. Park boundaries have been shifted, their areas reduced, to move valuable timber, mineral or water resources outside and available for exploitation. And governments have been accused of deliberately delaying the opening up and development of some of the big wilderness parks to prevent the public from acquiring an affection for them which would make logging or mining encroachments more difficult to justify.

As a result, while the *number* of parks keeps increasing because of the addition of small areas, the total acreage of B.C. provincial parks has been whittled down almost by half—from 11 million acres in 1945 to six-and-a-half million acres in 1970. And in the process, some of the key primitive features in the parks that remain have been destroyed.

Two of the province's finest primitive parks were in the coastal region—Tweedsmuir Park, a huge, wild, mountain area straddling the Coast Mountains, 300 miles north of Vancouver; and Strathcona Park, half a million acres of mountains, coastal rivers and rain forest in the centre of Vancouver Island. Both are parks little used as yet because of their remoteness and inaccessibility, but they originally possessed unique attractions for the not-too-distant time when expanding roads and growing population would bring them into the orbit of park users. But both are now examples of valuable park recreational assets that were bargained away for resource-dollar grabs.

Tweedsmuir Park's finest asset, the main reason for its establishment in 1938, was its great 200-mile circle of lakes and channels, walled by mountains, one of the most beautiful inland waterways in Canada. The water level over most of this vast lake chain—350 square miles of water surface—was raised by

Open pit mining is one of the most destructive methods available.

This model of the Fraser River helps scientists study its movement.

dams and the lakes turned into a mammoth reservoir to produce hydro-electric power for the aluminum smelters of Kitimat. Such flooding and the seasonally fluctuating water levels that characterize hydro-power reservoirs destroy natural shorelines and seriously reduce their recreational value. But Kitimat was of tremendous economic importance, probably justifying the flooding of Tweedsmuir's lakes; in any case, some of their recreational potential might still have been salvaged. But the manner in which the flooding was done has doomed the lakes of Tweedsmuir as a recreational waterway for generations to come. For haste and economy, forests along the lakeshores were not cleared prior to the flooding, but were left to be drowned by the rising waters. The result is hundreds of miles of shoreline turned into an impenetrable tangle of dead trees making boating, fishing and shore development impossible.

Strathcona Park, the biggest on Vancouver Island, fourth biggest in the province, has been logged in places but has virgin stands of Douglas fir rain forest in many of its rugged and as-yet inaccessible mountain valleys. If they can be preserved until roads make the park accessible, Strathcona's Douglas fir will join Cathedral Grove, Washington state's Olympic Park and California's redwoods as one of the famous big-tree showplaces of the continent.

But one of Strathcona's biggest attractions, in effect its "front door," was narrow, 18-mile Buttle Lake along the eastern boundary nearest to the towns and highways of Vancouver Island's inner, east coast. Buttle Lake, enclosed by steep, timbered slopes reaching to alpine peaks almost 7,000 feet high and fed by mountain streams tumbling down through box canyons, is the largest lake in the park and it originally provided water access to a wild and primitive region. But Buttle Lake had other coveted values.

Early in the 1950's, despite vigorous public opposition, the B.C. Power Commission was allowed to dam the outlet and raise the lake level ten feet. Beaches and picturesque box canyons were flooded, natural shore growth killed by seasonal fluctuations in water levels, and a scenic lake transformed into an ugly, muddy reservoir.

One such encroachment becomes a precedent and excuse for more. The next one was a mine, at the head of Buttle Lake, deep within the park. It was to be only a small mine, the government promised, requiring only a few acres, and it would not be permitted to encroach on park aesthetics or recreational values. But the mine operation has spawned the following: a ten-acre open-pit mine, a ten-acre tailing pond, a concentrating plant, a 25-mile mining road along one shore and around the end of Buttle Lake, a dam, powerhouse and transmission lines, a 1,000-foot pipeline out over Buttle Lake and the discharge of mine tailings and sewage into the lake, the polluting effect of which on fish and other aquatic life is yet unknown.

So Strathcona Park still has a large, beautiful, pristine hinterland, but the despoiling of Buttle Lake has transformed its entranceway into a shambles. It is like a splendid cathedral with its superb Gothic front door shattered and a blacksmith shop doing business in the foyer.

British Columbia governments have argued that the whole province is one huge park, that there is no urgent need for rigid park protection at this stage of the province's development. Southern Ontario and many U.S. states once said that too—and they kept on saying it until man's purblind and fanatical zeal for swamping the landscape with his handiwork left him imprisoned behind concrete walls and traffic jams in a dowdy, artificial cage of his own making. All across the continent, older jurisdictions are now buying back and re-creating at exorbitant cost samples of the vanishing nature that a naive and pioneering scramble for progress destroyed. British Columbia still has time to learn the lesson.

Born in a crucible of subterranean fire, sculptured by creeping seas, gigantic mountain-building squeezes and a million years of ice, adorned with a flora and fauna fashioned through millenia of natural selection and adaptation, it is Canada's loveliest province, and its coast is its loveliest part.

No region of Canada has more to cherish, or more to guard against profiteers seeking public resources for private gain. The necessities of tomorrow will not be bread alone—nor dividends, mines, mills, superports and an ever-growing Gross National Product. A jaded, technology-sated people are beginning to demand, and will demand more vociferously in the future, their lost heritage, the old dividends of the spirit, clean air, clean water, ancient forests, skeins of geese against an ocean sunset, and the languid wakes of sea otters once more off Vancouver Island where the heedless harvest began just 200 years ago.

GEOLOGIC TIME SCALE

TIME (MILLIONS OF YEARS)	ERA	PERIOD	EPOCH	THE ASCENT OF LIFE:
	CENOZOIC	QUATERNARY	PLEISTOCENE	
		TERTIARY	PLIOCENE	
			MIOCENE	
			OLIGOCENE	
50			EOCENE	
			PALEOCENE	
100	MESOZOIC	CRETACEOUS	UPPER	
			LOWER	
150		JURASSIC	UPPER / MIDDLE / LOWER	
200		TRIASSIC	UPPER / MIDDLE / LOWER	
250	PALAEOZOIC	PERMIAN	UPPER / MIDDLE / LOWER	
300		PENNSYLVANIAN		
350		MISSISSIPPIAN		
		DEVONIAN	UPPER / MIDDLE / LOWER	
400		SILURIAN		
450		ORDOVICIAN	UPPER / MIDDLE / LOWER	
500		CAMBRIAN	UPPER / MIDDLE / LOWER	
550				

THE ASCENT OF LIFE: 1, *protozoan*; 2, *jellyfish*; 3, *crinoid*; 4, *cephalopod*; 5, *climatius*; 6, *shark*; 7, *brachiopod*; 8, *seed fern*; 9, *dimetrodon*; 10, *brontosaurus*; 11, *plesiosaur*; 12, *tyrannosaurus*; 13, *taeniolabis*; 14, *diatryma*; 15, *hyracotherium*; 16, *brontotherium*; 17, *oxydactylus*; 18, *pliohippus*; 19, *mastodon*; 20, *man.*

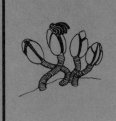

SHORT LIST OF ROCKS, PLANTS AND ANIMALS

The lists on the following pages have been compiled as a basic guide for amateur naturalists intending to explore the wealth of natural history of the Pacific Coast. These selected summaries cannot possibly cover all species — there are many thousands of insects alone — but an attempt has been made to include the common life forms and the natural phenomena peculiar to this region. Readers should find it useful to study the lists touching on their sphere of interest, checking off items they have observed during field trips. Those wishing to extend their search will find an extensive Bibliography on pages 153-5; references listed there contain more detailed information on specific subjects.

ROCKS

CENOZOIC ERA

RECENT AND PLEISTOCENE EPOCHS
Breccia
Clay
Gravel
Olivine-basalt
Pumice
Sand
Till
Tuff

TERTIARY PERIOD
Basaltic lava
Sandstone
Shale

MESOZOIC ERA

CRETACEOUS PERIOD
Sandstone
Shale

JURASSIC PERIOD
Granite
Granodiorite
Quartz-diorite
Syenite

JURASSIC-TRIASSIC PERIODS
(UNDIFFERENTIATED)
Argillite
Breccia
Lava
Sandstone
Tuff

PALEOZOIC ERA

PERMIAN PERIOD
Argillite
Chert
Lava
Limestone
Tuff

MISSISSIPPIAN TO CAMBRIAN
PERIODS (UNDIFFERENTIATED)
Argillite
Limestone
Quartzite
Shale

MINERALS

The minerals listed are those most likely to be found in the following regions.

QUEEN CHARLOTTE ISLANDS
Agate
Chalcedony
Garnet
Placer gold
Platinum

ZEBALLOS, VANCOUVER
ISLAND
Arsenopyrite
Flake gold
Quartz crystals
Sphalerite

TEXADA ISLAND,
STRAIT OF GEORGIA
Bornite
Chalcopyrite
Diopside
Epidote
Garnet
Gold
Magnetite
Marble

Molybdenite
Pyrrhotite
Silver
Tetrahedrite
Tremolite

COWICHAN LAKE,
VANCOUVER ISLAND
ISLAND
Garnet
Jasper
Rhodochrosite
Rhodonite

VICTORIA AREA
Agate
Jasper
Placer gold
Talc

GRAVEL BARS,
LOWER FRASER RIVER,
CHILLIWACK TO HOPE
Jade (nephrite)
Jasper
Placer gold
Quartz (dark blue)
Rhodonite

CHILKO LAKE
Petrified wood

PLANTS

SEAWEEDS

GREEN ALGAE
CHLOROPHYCEAE

Green confetti
Enteromorpha compressa

Green ball
Cladophora trichotoma

Green rope
Spongomorpha coalita

Sea fern
Bryopsis corticulans

Sea lettuce
Ulva fenestrata
Ulva lactuca

Spongy cushion
Codium setchellii

BROWN ALGAE
PHAEOPHYCEAE

Tar spot
Ralfsia pacifica

Fir needle
Heterochordaria abietina

Loose colour changer
Desmarestia intermedia

Brown sieve
Punctaria latifolia

Oyster thief
Colpomenia sinuosa

Stick bag
Coilodesme bulligera

Sea girdle or tangle
Laminaria platymeris

Sugar wrack
Laminaria saccharina

Sea colander
Agarum fimbriatum

Feather boa
Egregia menziesii

Rockweed or popping wrack
Fucus gardneri

Bladder leaf
Cystophyllum geminatum

Chain bladder
Cystoseira geminata

Jap-weed
Sargassum muticum

RED ALGAE
RHODOPHYCEAE

Red or purple laver
Porphyra perforata

Red fringe
Smithora naiadum

Cup and saucer
Constantinea simplex

Nail brush
Endocladia muricata

Red rock crust
Lithothamnium philippi

Coral alga
Corallina vancouveriensis

Bead corals
Calliarthron regenerans

Pointed lynx
Grateloupia pinnata

Lyall's seaweed
Prionitis lyallii

Red sea fan
Callophyllis edentata

Sea rose
Schizymenia pacifica

Coulter's seaweed
Agardhiella tenera

Ahnfelt's seaweed
Ahnfeltia concinna

Grapestone
Gigartina cristata

Turkish towel
Gigartina exasperata

Iridescent seaweeds
Iridaea cordata
Iridaea lincare

Sea sac
Halosaccion glandiforme

Dulse or red kale
Rhodymenia palmata

Hooked rope
Antithamnion uncinatum

Beauty bush
Callithamnion pikeanum

Pottery seaweed
Ceramium pacificum

Coarse sea lace
Microcladia borealis

Red wings
Ptilota filicina

Baron Delessert
Delesseria decipiens

Crisscross network
Polyneura latissima

Veined fan
Hymenena flabelligera

Polly Pacific
Polysiphonia pacifica

Baby angel wing
Pterosiphonia gracilis

Sea laurel
Laurencia spectabilis

Black pine
Rhodomela larix

SEA GRASSES

Eel grass
Zostera marina

Surf grass
Phyllospadix scouleri

WATER PLANTS

HERBS

Richardson's pondweed
Potamogeton richardsonii

Lesser duckweed
Lemna minor

Yellow pond lily
Nuphar variegatum

Common St. John's wort
Hypericum perforatum

Common bladderwort
Utricularia vulgaris

MARSH AND BOG PLANTS

SEDGES

Sedges
Carex (approx. 40 species)

GRASSES

Wild ryes
Elymus (several species)

Manna grasses
Glyceria (several species)

Alkali grass
Puccinellia pumila

RUSHES

Juncus (several species)

Wood rushes
Luzula (several species)

HERBS

Common horsetail
Equisetum arvense

Rattlesnake fern
Botrychium virginianum

Cotton grasses
Eriophorum (several species)

Marsh bulrush
Scirpus paludosus

Broadleafed cat-tail
Typha latifolia

Seashore sandwort
Honkenya peploides

Campions and catchflys
Silene (several species)

Yellow watercress
Rorippa islandica

Water hemlock
Cicuta douglasii

Wild carrot
Daucus carota

Water parsley
Oenanthe sarmentosa

Water parsnip
Sium cicutaefolium

Sea milkwort
Glaux maritima

Tufted losestrife
Lysimachia thrysiflora
Bugleweed
Lycopus uniflorus
Canada mint
Mentha arvensis
Heal-all
Prunella vulgaris
One-flowered cancer root
Orobanche uniflora

TERRESTRIAL PLANTS

SEDGES

Carex (approx. 40 species)

GRASSES

Bentgrasses
Agrostis (several species)
Little hair grass
Aira praecox
Water foxtail
Alopecurus geniculatus
Bromegrasses
Bromus (several species)
Drooping woodreed
Cinna latifolia
Orchard grass
Dactylis glomerata
Saltgrass
Distichlis spicata
Perennial ryegrass
Lolium perenne
Alaska onion-grass
Melica subulata

Timothy grasses
Phleum (several species)
Bluegrasses
Poa (several species)

HERBS

Ground pine
Lycopodium clavatum
Maidenhair fern
Adiantum pedatum

Maidenhair spleenwort
Asplenium trichomanes
Lady fern
Athyrium filix-femina
Deer fern
Blechnum spicant
Parsley fern
Cryptogramma crispa
Fragile fern
Cystopteris fragilis
Spiny wood fern
Dryopteris austriaca
Oak fern
Gymnocarpium dryopteris
Golden-back fern
Pityrogramma triangularis

Common polypody
Polypodium vulgare
Holly fern
Polystichum lonchitis
Bracken
Pteridium aquilinum
Giant chain fern
Woodwardia fimbriata
Skunk cabbage
Lysichiton kamtschatcense
Nodding onion
Allium cernuum
Large-flowered brodiaea
Brodiaea grandiflora
Common camas
Camassia quamash
Hooker's fairy bells
Disporum hookeri
White easter lily
Erythronium oregonum
Chocolate lily
Fritillaria lanceolata
Tiger lily
Lilium columbianum
Wild lily-of-the-valley
Maianthemum dilatatum
False Solomon's seal
Smilacina racemosa

Twisted stalk
Streptopus amplexifolius
Western trillium
Trillium ovatum
Death camas
Zygadenus venenosus
Calypso
Calypso bulbosa
Western coral-root
Corallorhiza mertensiana
Helleborine
Epipactis helleborine
Green-leafed rattlesnake orchid
Goodyera oblongifolia
Large round-leafed orchid
Habenaria orbiculata
Hooded ladies' tresses
Spiranthes romanzoffiana
Stinging nettle
Urtica dioica
Wild ginger
Asarum caudatum
Lamb's quarters
Chenopodium album
Spotted knotweed
Polygonum persicaria
Sheep sorrel
Rumex acetosella
Starworts
Stellaria (several species)
Red baneberry
Actaea rubra
Columbine
Aquilegia formosa
Larkspur
Delphinium menziesii

Buttercups
Ranunculus (many species)
Meadow rue
Thalictrum occidentale

False bugbane
Trautvetteria caroliniensis
Bleeding heart
Dicentra formosa
Rock cresses
Arabis (several species)
Yellow rocket
Barbarea vulgaris
Sea rocket
Cakile edentula
Shepherd's purse
Capsella bursa-pastoris
Wormseed mustard
Erysimum cheiranthoides
Peppergrasses
Lepidium (several species)
Stonecrops
Sedum (several species)
Alumroot
Heuchera glabra
Small-flowered fringe cup
Lithophragma parviflora
Rusty saxifrage
Saxifraga occidentalis
Fringe cups
Tellima (several species)
Foam flower
Tiarella trifoliata
Youth-on-age
Tolmiea menziesii
Coast strawberry
Fragaria chiloensis
Large-leafed avens
Geum macrophyllum

Silverweed
Potentilla anserina
Beach pea
Lathyrus japonicus
Lupines
Lupinus (several species)
Black medick
Medicago lupulina
White sweet clover
Melilotus alba

Clovers
Trifolium (many species)
Vetches
Vicia (many species)
Wild geraniums
Geranium (several species)
Blue violet
Viola adunca
Prickly pear cactus
Opuntia fragilis
Enchanter's nightshade
Circaea alpina
Fireweed
Epilobium angustifolium
Angelica
Angelica genuflexa
Cow parsnip
Heracleum lanatum
Indian consumption plant
Lomatium nudicaule
Sweet cicely
Osmorhiza chilensis
Snakeroots
Sanicula (several species)
Candystick
Allotropa virgata
Pipsissewa
Chimaphila umbellata
Pinesap
Hypopitys monotropa
One-flowered wintergreen
Moneses uniflora
Indian pipe
Monotropa uniflora
Pinedrops
Ptersopora andromedea
Large wintergreen
Pyrola asarifolia
Shooting stars
Dodecatheon (several species)
Star flower
Trientalis latifolia
Gentians
Gentiana (several species)
Spreading dogbane
Apocynum androsaemifolium
Collomia
Collomia grandiflora
Small-flowered nemophila
Nemophila parviflora
Varied-leafed phacelia
Phacelia heterophylla
Borage
Amsinckia retrorsa

Forget-me-not
Myosotis arvensis
Hedge nettle
Stachys ciliosa
Indian paintbrush
Castilleja angustifolia
Large-flowered blue-eyed Mary
Collinsia grandiflora
Butter and eggs
Linaria vulgaris
Musk flower
Mimulus moschatus
Sickletop lousewort
Pedicularis racemosa
Cascade penstemon
Penstemon serrulatus
Mullein
Verbascum thapsus
Brooklime
Veronica americana

Common plantain
Plantago major
Small bedstraw
Galium trifidum
Bluebell
Campanula rotundifolia
Yarrow
Achillea millefolium
Silvergreen
Adenocaulon bicolor
Pale agoseris
Agoseris glauca
Pussytoes
Antennaria (several species)
Burdock
Arctium minus
Arnicas
Arnica (several species)
Cut-leafed wormwood
Artemisia campestris

Asters
Aster (several species)

Stick-tight
Bidens cernua
Oxeye daisy
Chrysanthemum leucanthemum
Canada thistle
Cirsium arvense
Horseweed
Erigeron canadensis
Woolly sunflower
Eriophyllum lanatum
Gumweed
Grindelia integrifolia
Hawkweeds
Hieracium (several species)
Tall blue lettuce
Lactuca spicata
Silverback
Luina hypoleuca
Pineapple-weed
Matricaria matricarioides
Coltsfoot
Petasites speciosa
Groundsels and ragworts
Senecio (several species)
Canadian goldenrod
Solidago canadensis
Perennial sow-thistle
Sonchus arvensis
Prickly sow-thistle
Sonchus asper
Common sow-thistle
Sonchus oleraceus
Tansy
Tanacetum vulgare
Dandelion
Taraxacum officinale
SHRUBS
Bunchberry
Cornus canadensis

Cascara
Rhamnus purshiana
Pacific flowering dogwood
Cornus nuttallii
Arbutus
Arbutus menziesii
Stink currant
Ribes bracteosum
Wild gooseberry
Ribes divaricatum
Gummy gooseberry
Ribes lobbii
Red-flowered currant
Ribes sanguineum
Mock orange
Philadelphus gordonianus
Pacific serviceberry
Amelanchier florida
Goat's beard
Aruncus sylvester
Ocean spray
Holodiscus discolor
Indian plum
Osmaronia cerasiformis
Ninebark
Physocarpus discolor

Sweetbrier
Rosa eglanteria
Dwarf rose
Rosa gymnocarpa
Common wild rose
Rosa nutkana
Scotch broom
Cytisus scoparius
Gorse
Ulex europaeus
Buckbrush
Ceanothus sanguineus
Snowbrush
Ceanothus velutinus
False box
Pachystima myrsinites

Soapberry
Shepherdia canadensis

Devil's club
Oplopanax horridus

Western dogwood
Cornus occidentalis

Bog rosemary
Andromeda polifolia

Hairy manzanita
Arctostaphylos columbiana

Copper bush
Cladothamnus pyrolaeflorus

Salal
Gaultheria shallon

Swamp laurel
Kalmia polifolia

Labrador tea
Ledum groenlandicum

False azalea
Menziesia ferruginea

Alaska blueberry
Vaccinium alaskaense

Dwarf blueberry
Vaccinium caespitosum

Western blueberry
Vaccinium occidentale

Tall huckleberry
Vaccinium ovalifolium

Evergreen huckleberry
Vaccinium ovatum

Red huckleberry
Vaccinium parvifolium

Bog blueberry
Vaccinium uliginosum

Black twinberry
Lonicera involucrata

Red twinberry
Lonicera utahensis

Blueberry elder
Sambucus glauca

Redberry elder
Sambucus racemosa

Waxberry
Symphoricarpos albus

Squashberry
Viburnum edule

VINES

Tall mahonia
Mahonia aquifolium

Oregon grape
Mahonia nervosa

Creeping mahonia
Mahonia repens

Trailing black currant
Ribes laxiflorum

Trailing blackberry
Rubus ursinus

Poison oak
Rhus diversiloba

Kinnikinnick
Arctostaphylos uva-ursi

Western teaberry
Gaultheria ovatifolia

Bog cranberry
Oxycoccus quadripetalus

Mountain cranberry
Vaccinium vitis-idaea

Twinflower
Linnaea borealis

Orange honeysuckle
Lonicera ciliosa

Red honeysuckle
Lonicera dioica

Purple honeysuckle
Lonicera hispidula

TREES

CONIFEROUS TREES

Amabilis fir
Abies amabilis

Grand fir
Abies grandis

Rocky mountain juniper
Juniperus scopulorum

Sitka spruce
Picea sitchensis

Shore pine
Pinus contorta

Western white pine
Pinus monticola

Douglas fir
Pseudotsuga menziesii

Pacific yew
Taxus brevifolia

Western red cedar
Thuja plicata

Western hemlock
Tsuga heterophylla

DECIDUOUS TREES

Trembling aspen
Populus tremuloides

Black cottonwood
Populus trichocarpa

Pacific willow
Salix lasiandra

Red alder
Alnus rubra

Western white birch
Betula papyrifera

Garry oak
Quercus garryana

Black hawthorn
Crataegus douglasii

Pacific crabapple
Malus diversifolia

Bitter cherry
Prunus emarginata

Western choke cherry
Prunus virginiana

European mountain ash
Sorbus aucuparia

Vine maple
Acer circinatum

Douglas maple
Acer glabrum

Broadleaf maple
Acer macrophyllum

Coyote willow
Salix exigua

Geyer willow
Salix geyeriana

Hooker willow
Salix hookeriana

Mackenzie willow
Salix mackenziana

Bog willow
Salix pedicellaris

Scouler willow
Salix scouleriana

Sitka willow
Salix sitchensis

Wax-myrtle
Myrica californica

Sweet gale
Myrica gale

Dwarf birch
Betula glandulosa

Swamp birch
Betula pumila

Hazelnut
Corylus cornuta

Swamp rose
Rosa pisocarpa

Evergreen blackberry
Rubus laciniatus

Black raspberry
Rubus leucodermis

Thimbleberry
Rubus parviflorus

Himalayan blackberry
Rubus procerus

Salmonberry
Rubus spectabilis

Hardhack
Spiraea douglasii

SUB ALPINE AND ALPINE PLANTS

HERBACEOUS FLOWERING PLANTS

Queen's cup
Clintonia uniflora

Snow lily
Erythronium grandiflorum
Indian hellebore
Veratrum viride
Alpine bistort
Polygonum viviparum
Moss campion
Silene acaulis
Alpine anemone
Anemone drummondii
White marsh marigold
Caltha leptosepala
Snow buttercup
Ranunculus eschscholtzii
Globe flower
Trollius laxus
Leptarrhena
Leptarrhena pyrolifolia
Fringed grass-of-parnassus
Parnassia fimbriata
Spotted saxifrage
Saxifraga bronchialis
Lyall's saxifrage
Saxifraga lyallii
Tolmie saxifrage
Saxifraga tolmiei
Simple-leafed foam flower
Tiarella unifoliata
Fanleaf cinquefoil
Potentilla flabellifolia
Broadleaf lupine
Lupinus latifolius
Low lupine
Lupinus lepidus
Evergreen violet
Viola orbiculata
Alpine fireweed
Epilobium alpinum
Spreading phlox
Phlox diffusa
Mountain phacelia
Phacelia sericea
Indian paintbrushes
Castilleja (several alpine
    species)
Red monkey flower
Mimulus lewisii
Alpine monkey flower
Mimulus tilingii
Wood betony
Pedicularis bracteosa
Elephant head
Pedicularis groenlandica

Menzies penstemon
Penstemon davidsonii
Alpine speedwell
Veronica wormskjoldii
Dwarf mountain fleabane
Erigeron compositus
Mountain daisy
Erigeron peregrinus
Slender hawkweed
Hieracium gracile
Alpine coltsfoot
Petasites frigidus
Giant ragwort
Senecio triangularis
SHRUBS AND WOODY CREEPERS
Common juniper
Juniperus communis
Alpine willow
Salix arctica
Barclay willow
Salix barclayi
Sitka alder
Alnus sinuata
Maple-leaf currant
Ribes acerifolium

Swamp gooseberry
Ribes lacustre
Mountain gooseberry
Ribes montigenum
Mountain spirea
Spiraea densiflora
Meadow spirea
Luetkea pectinata
Sub-alpine blackberry
Rubus nivalis
Trailing rubus
Rubus pedatus
Sitka mountain ash
Sorbus sitchensis
Crowberry
Empetrum nigrum
White moss heather
Cassiope mertensiana

Alaska moss heather
Cassiope stelleriana
Alpine wintergreen
Gaultheria humifusa
Alpine azalea
Loiseleuria procumbens
Pink mountain heather
Phyllodoce empetriformis
Yellow mountain heather
Phyllodoce glanduliflora
White-flowered rhododendron
Rhododendron albiflorum
Dwarf bilberry
Vaccinium deliciosum
Mountain bilberry
Vaccinium membranaceum
Menzies penstemon
Penstemon davidsonii
TREES
Alpine fir
Abies lasiocarpa
Yellow cedar
Chamaecyparis nootkatensis
Whitebark pine
Pinus albicaulis
Mountain hemlock
Tsuga mertensiana

ANIMALS

SEA AND INTER-TIDAL ANIMALS
Sponges
Porifera (approx. 25 species)
HYDROIDS, JELLYFISH, SEA
ANEMONES AND CORALS
COELENTERATA
Sea plume
Obelia dichotoma

Sea jellyfish
Aquorea aquorea
Moon jellyfish
Aurelia labiata
Sea blubber
Cyanea capillata
Great green anemone
Anthopleura xanthogrammica
Warty anemone
Cribina xanthogrammica
Flatworms
Platyhelminthes
Ribbon worms
Nemertea
Segmented worms
Annelida
Plume worm
Eudistylia vancouveri
Pile worm
Nereis vexillosa

Mollusks
Mollusca
CHITONS, LIMPETS AND SNAILS
The Univalves
Fingered limpet
Acmaea digitalis
Whitecap limpet
Acmaea mitra
Shield limpet
Acmaea pelta
Mask limpet
Acmaea persona
Plate limpet
Acmaea testudinalis

Northern abalone
Haliotis kamtschatkana
Rough keyhole limpet
Diodora aspera
Spotted keyhole limpet
Megatabennus bimaculatus
Black top-shell
Tegula funebralis
Ringed top-shell
Calliostoma annulatum

Smooth margarite
Margarites helicinus
Lirulate margarite
Margarites lirulatus
Carpenter dwarf turban
Homalopoma carpenteri
Sitka littorine
Littorina sitkana
Checkered littorine
Littorina scutulata
Variegated chink-shell
Lacuna variegata
Threaded bittium
Bittium eschrichtii
Slender bittium
Bittium attenuatum
Cuming's batillaria
Batillaria zonalis
Flat hoof-shell
Hipponix cranoides
Chinese hat snail
Calyptraea fastigiata
Hooked slipper-shell
Crepidula adunca
Wrinkled slipper-shell
Crepidula lingulata
White slipper-shell
Crepidula nummaria
Lewis' moon-snail
Polinices lewisii
Bull's-eye
Natica clausa
Velvet shell
Velutina laevigata
Checkered hairy snail
Trichotropis cancellata
Oregon triton
Fusitriton oregonensis
Odostome
Odostomia quadrae
Eschscholtz turbonilla
Turbonilla eschscholtzi
Red melanella
Eulima rutila
Spindle shell
Searlesia dira

Channeled dog whelk
Nassarius fossatus
Lean dog whelk
Nassarius mendicus
Black dog whelk
Nassarius obsoletus
Leafy hornmouth
Ceratostoma foliata
Lurid rock-shell
Ocenebra lurida

Sculptured rock-shell
Ocenebra interfossa
Japanese oyster drill
Ocenebra japonica
Wrinkled purple
Thais lamellosa
Short-spired purple
Thais emarginata
Rough purple
Thais lima
Wrinkled amphissa
Amphissa columbiana
Dove shell
Mitrella gausapata
Purple olive
Olivalla biplicata
Little olive
Olivella baetica
Pear-shaped marginella
Cypraeolina pyriformis
Pillowed lathe-shell
Acteocina culcitella
Barrel shell
Acteon punctocoelatus
White bubble-shell
Haminaea vesicula
Siphon shell
Siphonaria thersites
OYSTERS, SCALLOPS AND CLAMS
The Bivalves
Ark shell
Glycymeris subobsoleta

Rock oyster
Pododesmus macroschisma
Edible mussel
Mytilus edulis
California mussel
Mytilus californianus
Giant horse mussel
Modiolus rectus
Giant Pacific scallop
Pecten caurinus
Purple-hinged rock scallop
Hinnites multirugosus
Pacific oyster
Crassostrea gigas
Atlantic oyster
Crassostrea virginica
Native oyster
Ostrea lurida
Salmon tellen
Tellina salmonea
Button tellen
Tellina buttoni
Carpenter tellen
Tellina carpenteri
Inconspicuous macoma
Macoma inconspicua
Sand clam
Macoma secta
Bent-nose clam
Macoma nasuta
Polluted macoma
Macoma irus
Red-painted semele
Semele rubropicta
Razor clam
Siliqua patula
Jack-knife clam
Solen sicarius
Horse clam
Schizothaerus nuttalli
Horse clam
Schizothaerus capax
Cockel
Clinocardium nuttalli

Sunset shell
Gari californica
Native little-neck clam
Protothaca staminea
Manila clam
Venerupis japonica
Butter clam
Saxidomus giganteus
Little transennella
Transennella tantilla
Lord pebble shell
Psephidia lordi
Round diplodon
Diplodonta orbellus
Puget Sound lyonsia
Lyonsia pugettensis
Rock-dwell entodesma
Entodesma saxicola
Sea bottle shell
Mytilimeria nuttalli
LaPerouse Kelly shell
Kellia laperousi
Rough wrinkled lepton
Pseudopythina rugifera
False mya
Cryptomya californica
Mud clam
Mya arenaria
Blunt soft-shell clam
Mya truncata
Chubby mya
Platydon cancellatus
Geoduck
Panope generosa
Gallic saxicave
Hiatella gallicana
Nestling saxicave
Hiatella pholadis
Piddock
Penitella penita
Oval piddock
Penitella gabbi
Pilsbry piddock
Zirphaea pilsbryi
Pacific shipworm
Bankia setacea
NUDIBRANCHES, SQUIDS
AND OCTOPI
The Shell-less Mollusks
Sea lemon
Anisodoris nobilis
Hooded nudibranch
Chioraera leonina

Ringed nudibranch
Dialula sandiegensis
Opalescent nudibranch
Hermissenda crassicornis
Opalescent squid
Loligo opalescens
Octopus
Octopus apollyon

Crustaceans
Crustacea

ACORN BARNACLES
Thatched barnacle
Balanus cariosus
Smooth acorn barnacle
Balanus crenatus
Giant barnacle
Balanus nubilis
Balanus balanus
Balanus glandulus
Balanus hesperius
Balanus rostratus
Chthamalus dalli
WHALE BARNACLES
Coronula diadema
Coronula reginae
Cryptolepas rachianecti
Xenobalanus globicipitis

GOOSE OR STALKED BARNACLES
Lepas anatifera
Lepas fascicularis
Lepas hilli
Lepas pectinata
Mitella polymerus
Scalpellum columbianum
SHRIMPS, CRABS AND RELATIVES
DECAPODA
Transparent isopod
Idothea resecata
Olive green isopod
Idothea wasnesenskii
Sea slater
Ligyda pallasii

Sand hoppers
Sand fleas
Phantom shrimp
Caprella kennerlyi
Black-tailed shrimp
Crago nigricauda
Coon-striped shrimp
Pandalus danae
Spirontocaris shrimps
Ghost shrimp
Callianassa gigas
Hairy crab
Hapalogaster mertensii
Hermit crabs
Pagurus
Porcelain crab
Petrolisthes cinctipes
Marine crayfish
Upogebia pugettensis
Edible crab
Cancer magister
Hairy cancer crab
Cancer oregonensis
Red rock crab
Cancer productus
Purple shore crab
Hemigrapsus nudus
Hairy shore crab
Hemigrapsus oregonensis
Black-clawed crab
Lophopanopeus bellus
Graceful kelp crab
Pugettia gracilis
Northern kelp crab
Pugettia productus
Horse crab
Telmessus cheiragonus
STARFISH AND RELATIVES
ECHINODERMA
Rose star
Crossaster papposus
Leather star
Dermasterias imbricata
Mottled star
Evasterias troschelii

Blood star
Henricia leviuscula
Six-rayed star
Leptasterias hexactis
Red star
Mediaster aequalis
Brittle star
Ophiopholis aculeata
Long-rayed star
Orthasterias koehleri
Broad-disk star
Patiria miniata
Purple star
Pisaster ochraceus
Sunflower star
Pycnopodia helianthoides
Red sun star
Solaster dawsoni
Sun star
Solaster stimpsoni
Sand dollar
Echinarachnius exentricus
Green sea urchin
Strongylocentrotus drobachiensis
Giant red urchin
Strongylocentrotus franciscanus
Purple sea urchin
Strongylocentrotus purpuratus
White sea gherkin
Cucumaria lubrica
Red sea gherkin
Cucumaria miniata

Giant sea cucumber
Stichopus californicus

MARINE FISHES

MACKEREL SHARKS
LAMNIDAE
Basking shark
Cetorhinus maximus
DOGFISH SHARKS
SQUALIDAE
Spiny dogfish
Squalus acanthias

SKATES
RAJIDAE
Big skate
Raja binoculata
CHIMAERAS
CHIMAERIDAE
Ratfish
Hydrolagus colliei
HERRINGS
CLUPEIDAE
Pacific herring
Clupea harengus pallasi
SALMONS AND TROUTS
SALMONIDAE
Steelhead trout
Salmo gairdneri
Coastal cutthroat trout
Salmo clarki
Coho salmon
Oncorhynchus kisutch
Chinook salmon
Oncorhynchus tshawytscha
Pink salmon
Oncorhynchus gorbuscha
Chum salmon
Oncorhynchus keta
Sockeye salmon
Oncorhynchus nerka
SMELTS
OSMERIDAE
Eulachon
Thaleichthys pacificus
Surf smelt
Hypomesus pretiosus
CODS
GADIDAE
Pacific hake
Meluccius productus
Walleye pollock
Theragra chalcogrammus
Pacific tomcod
Microgradus proximus
STICKLEBACKS
GASTEROSTEIDAE
Threespine stickleback
Gasterosteus aculeatus

TUBE-SNOUTS
AULORHYINCHIDAE
Tube-snout
Aulorhynchus flavidus

PIPEFISHES AND SEAHORSES
SYNGNATHIDAE
Bay pipefish
Syngnathus griseolineatus

SURFPERCHES
EMBIOTOCIDAE
Shiner perch
Cymatogaster aggregata
Striped seaperch
Embiotoca lateralis
Pile perch
Rhacochilus vacca

GOBIES
GOBIIDAE
Arrowgoby
Clevelandia ios

SCORPIONFISHES AND
ROCKFISHES
SCORPAENIDAE
Copper rockfish
Sebastodes caurinus
Bocaccio
Sebastodes paucispinis
Rasphad rockfish
Sebastodes ruberrimus
Black rockfish
Sebastodes melanops

SABLEFISHES
ANOPLOPOMATIDAE
Sablefish
Anoplopoma fimbria

GREENLINGS
HEXAGRAMMIDAE
Rock greenling
Hexagrammos superciliosus
Lingcod
Ophiodon elongatus

PRICKLEBACKS
STICHAEIDAE
Black prickleback
Xiphister atropurpureus

RIGHTEYE FLOUNDERS
PLEURONECTIDAE
Pacific halibut
Hippoglossus stenolepis
Starry flounder
Platichthys stellatus

LUMPFISHES AND SNAILFISHES
CYCLOPTERIDAE
Tidepool snailfish
Liparis florae

SAND LANCES
AMMODYTIDAE
Pacific sand lance
Ammodytes hexapterus

WOLFFISHES
ANARHICHADIDAE
Wolf-eel
Anarrhichthys ocellatus

CLINGFISHES
GOBIESOCIDAE
Northern clingfish
Gobiesox maeandricus

TOADFISHES
BATRACHOIDIDAE
Northern midshipman
Porichthys notatus

SCULPINS
COTTIDAE
Cabezon
Scorpaenichthys marmoratus
Red Irish lord
Hemilepidotus hemilepidotus
Tidepool sculpin
Oligocottus maculosus

Pacific staghorn sculpin
Leptocottus armatus
Sailfin sculpin
Nautichthys oculofasciatus
Grunt sculpin
Rhamphocottus richardsoni

AMPHIBIANS
Pacific coast newt
Taricha granulosa
Long-toed salamander
Ambystoma macrodactylum
Northwestern salamander
Ambystoma gracile
Pacific giant salamander
Dicamptodon ensatus

Western red-backed
  salamander
Plethodon vehiculum
Red salamander
Ensatina eschscholtzi
Clouded salamander
Aneides ferreus
Tailed toad
Ascaphus truei
Northwestern toad
Bufo boreas
Pacific tree-toad
Hyla regilla
Red-legged frog
Rana aurora

Bullfrog
Rana catesbeiana
Green frog
Rana clamitans

REPTILES
Western painted turtle
Chrysemys picta
Pacific leather-back turtle
Dermochelys coriacea
Northern alligator lizard
Gerrhonotus caeruleus
Three-lined garter snake
Thamnophis sirtalis
Puget garter snake
Thamnophis ordinoides
Coast garter snake
Thamnophis elegans

BIRDS
We have included only birds
whose breeding or migratory
range in Canada is chiefly
restricted to the coastal British
Columbia region. Complete
lists of birds of the area may
be obtained from British
Columbia Provincial Museum,
Victoria.

SEA, FRESHWATER AND
SHORE BIRDS
Black-footed albatross
Diomedea nigripes
Fulmar
Fulmarus glacialis
Pink-footed shearwater
Puffinus creatopus
Pale-footed shearwater
Puffinus carneipes
Sooty shearwater
Puffinus griseus
Slender-billed shearwater
Puffinus tenuirostris
Manx shearwater
Puffinus puffinus
Fork-tailed petrel
Oceanodroma furcata
Leach's petrel
Oceanodroma leucorhoa
Brandt's cormorant
Phalacrocorax penicillatus
Pelagic cormorant
Phalacrocorax pelagicus
Cinnamon teal
Anas cyanoptera
Barrow's goldeneye
Bucephala islandica
Harlequin duck
Histrionicus histrionicus
Black oystercatcher
Haematopus bachmani
Semipalmated plover
Charadrius semipalmatus
American golden plover
Pluvialis dominica
Black-bellied plover
Squatarola squatarola
Surfbird
Aphriza virgata
Black turnstone
Arenaria melanocephala

150

Wandering tattler
Heteroscelus incanum

Rock sandpiper
Erolia ptilocnemis

Sharp-tailed sandpiper
Erolia acuminata

Long-billed dowitcher
Limnodromus scolopaceus

Western sandpiper
Ereunetes mauri

Glaucous-winged gull
Larus glaucescens

Western gull
Larus occidentalis

Mew gull
Larus canus

Heermann's gull
Larus heermanni

Sabine's gull
Xema sabini

Pigeon guillemot
Cepphus columba

Marbled murrelet
Brachyramphus marmoratum

Ancient murrelet
Synthliboramphus antiquum

Cassin's auklet
Ptychoramphus aleutica

Rhinoceros auklet
Cerorhinca monocerata

Tufted puffin
Lunda cirrhata

BIRDS OF PREY

Bald eagle
Haliaeetus leucocephalus

Osprey
Pandion haliaetus

Peregrine falcon
Falco peregrinus

Sparrow hawk
Falco sparverius

Barn owl
Tyto alba

Pygmy owl
Glaucidium gnoma

Spotted owl
Strix occidentalis

LAND BIRDS

Blue grouse
Dendragapus obscurus

White-tailed ptarmigan
Lagopus leucurus

California quail
Lophortyx californicus

Mountain quail
Oreortyx pictus

Band-tailed pigeon
Columba fasciata

Black swift
Cypseloides niger

Vaux swift
Chaetura vauxi

Rufous hummingbird
Selasphorus rufus

Red-shafted flicker
Colaptes cafer

Lewis' woodpecker
Asyndesmus lewis

Hammond's flycatcher
Empidonax hammondii

Western flycatcher
Empidonax difficilis

Skylark
Alauda arvensis

Violet-green swallow
Tachycineta thalassina

Steller's jay
Cyanocitta stelleri

Northwestern crow
Corvus caurinus

Chestnut-backed chickadee
Parus rufescens

Common bushtit
Psaltriparus minimus

Dipper
Cinclus mexicanus

Bewick's wren
Thryomanes bewickii

Varied thrush
Ixoreus naevius

Western bluebird
Sialia mexicana

Northern shrike
Lanius excubitor

Crested mynah
Acridotheres cristatellus

Hutton's vireo
Vireo huttoni

Audubon's warbler
Dendroica auduboni

Black-throated gray warbler
Dendroica nigrescens

MacGillivray's warbler
Oporonis tolmiei

House finch
Carpodacus mexicanus

Gray-crowned rosy finch
Leucosticte tephrocotis

Golden-crowned sparrow
Zonotrichia atricapilla

Western meadowlark
Sturnella neglecta

Black-headed grosbeak
Pheucticus melanocephalus

MAMMALS
Marine Mammals

WHALES, PORPOISES AND
  DOLPHINS
CETACEA

Baird's beaked whale
Berardius bairdi

Sperm whale
Physeter catodon

Pacific striped dolphin
Lagenorhynchus obliquidens

Pacific killer whale
Orcinus rectipinna

Pilot whale
Globicephala scammoni

Harbour porpoise
Phocaena vomerina

Dall porpoise
Phocoenoides dalli

Gray whale
Eschrichtius glaucus

Common finback
Balaenoptera physalus

Sei whale
Balaenoptera borealis

Minke whale
Balaenoptera acutorostrata

Blue whale
Sibbaldus musculus

Humpback whale
Megaptera novaeangliae

Pacific right whale
Eubalaena sieboldi

SEALS AND SEA-LIONS
PINNIPEDIA

Northern fur seal
Callorhinus ursinus

Steller's sea-lion
Eumetopias jubata

Hair seal
Phoca vitulina

Elephant seal
Mirounga angustirostris

Land Mammals

SHREWS
SORICIDAE

Cinereus shrew
Sorex cinereus

Trowbridge shrew
Sorex trowbridgei

Wandering shrew
Sorex vagrans

Navigator shrew
Sorex palustris

Bendire shrew
Sorex bendirei

MOLES
TALPIDAE

Shrew-mole
Neurotrichus gibbsi

Coast mole
Scapanus orarius

BATS
VESPERTILIONIDAE

Western big-eared bat
Plecotus townsendi

Big brown bat
Eptesicus fuscus

Silver-haired bat
Lasionycteris noctivagans

Hoary bat
Lasiurus cinereus

California myotis
Myotis californicus

Long-eared myotis
Myotis evotis

Keen myotis
Myotis keeni

Little brown bat
Myotis lucifugus

Yuma myotis
Myotis yumanensis

PIKAS
OCHOTONIDAE

Rocky Mountain pika
Ochotona princeps

HARES
LEPORIDAE

Snowshoe hare
Lepus americanus

Eastern cottontail
Sylvilagus floridanus

MOUNTAIN BEAVERS
APLODONTIIDAE

Mountain beaver
Aplodontia rufa

OPOSSUMS
DIDELPHIDAE

American opossum
Didelphis marsupialis

SQUIRRELS
SCIURIDAE

Hoary marmot
Marmota caligata

Vancouver marmot
Marmota vancouverensis

Northwestern chipmunk
Eutamias amoenus

Townsend chipmunk
Eutamias townsendi

Gray squirrel
Sciurus carolinensis

Red squirrel
Tamiasciurus hudsonicus

Douglas squirrel
Tamiasciurus douglasi

Northern flying squirrel
Glaucomys sabrinus

BEAVERS
CASTORIDAE

American beaver
Castor canadensis

MICE
CRICETIDAE

Deer mouse
Peromyscus maniculatus

Cascade deer mouse
Peromyscus oreas

Bushy-tailed woodrat
Neotoma cinerea

Northern bog lemming
Synoptomys borealis

Boreal redback vole
Clethrionomys gapperi

Western redback vole
Clethrionomys occidentalis

Mountain heather vole
Phenacomys intermedius

Long-tailed vole
Microtus longicaudus

Creeping vole
Microtus oregoni

Richardson vole
Microtus richardsoni

Townsend vole
Microtus townsendi

Muskrat
Ondatra zibethica

OLD WORLD RATS AND MICE
MURIDAE

Norway rat
Rattus norvegicus

Black rat
Rattus rattus

House mouse
Mus musculus

JUMPING MICE
ZAPODIDAE

Northwestern jumping mouse
Zapus trinotatus

PORCUPINES
ERETHIZONTIDAE

Porcupine
Erethizon dorsatum

NUTRIAS
CAPROMYIDAE

Nutria
Myocaster coypus

WOLVES AND FOXES
CANIDAE

Coyote
Canis latrans

Timber wolf
Canis lupus

Red fox
Vulpes vulpes

BEARS
URSIDAE

Black bear
Ursus americanus

Grizzly bear
Ursus horribilis

RACCOONS
PROCYONIDAE

Raccoon
Procyon lotor

WEASELS, FERRETS AND MINKS
MUSTELIDAE

Marten
Martes americana

Fisher
Martes pennanti

Short-tailed weasel
Mustela erminea

Long-tailed weasel
Mustela frenata

Mink
Mustela vison

River otter
Lutra canadensis

Wolverine
Gulo luscus

Spotted skunk
Spilogale putorius

Striped skunk
Mephitis mephitis

CATS
FELIDAE

Cougar
Felis concolor

Bobcat
Lynx rufus

CATTLE
BOVIDAE

Mountain goat
Oreamnos americanus

DEER
CERVIDAE

Roosevelt elk
Cervus canadensis

Blacktail deer
Odocoileus hemionus

Moose
Alces alces

BIBLIOGRAPHY

REGIONAL

Beautiful British Columbia.
Victoria: Department of Travel Industry.

British Columbia Atlas of Resources.
Victoria: British Columbia Natural
Resources Conference, 1956.

CAMPBELL, WAYNE and STIRLING, DAVID.
*Notes on the Natural History of Cleland
Island.* 1968.

*Challenge in Abundance: A Panorama of
British Columbia Life.*
Victoria: British Columbia Centennial
Committee, 1967.

CHAPMAN, J. D.
The Climate of British Columbia.
Victoria: Transactions, Fifth British
Columbia Natural Resources Conference,
1952.

EDWARDS, R. Y. (editor).
Naturalist's Guide to the Victoria Region.
Victoria: Victoria Natural History Society,
1967.

THETIS PARK NATURE SANCTUARY
ASSOCIATION.
Natural History of Thetis Lake Area.
Victoria: Provincial Museum, reprinted from
1965 annual report.

This is British Columbia.
Victoria: Department of Travel Industry,
1967.

Transactions (annually since 1948).
Victoria: British Columbia Natural
Resources Conference.

Vancouver Aquarium Newsletter.
Vancouver: Public Aquarium Association.

Vancouver Natural History Society Bulletin.

Victoria Naturalist.
Victoria: Victoria Natural History Society.

Wildlife Review.
Victoria: Fish and Wildlife Branch,
Department of Recreation and Conservation.

GEOLOGY

BOSTOCK, H. S.
Physiography of the Canadian Cordillera.
Ottawa: Geological Survey of Canada,
Mem. 247, 1948.

FLINT, R. F.
Glacial and Pleistocene Geology.
New York: John Wiley and Sons, 1957.

Geology and Economic Minerals of Canada.
Ottawa: Geological Survey of Canada,
Economic Series No. 1, 1957.

*Guidebook for Geological Field Trips in
Southwestern British Columbia.*
Vancouver: Geological Discussion Club,
1960.

HOLLAND, STUART S.
Landforms of British Columbia.
Victoria: Department of Mines, Bulletin
No. 48, 1964.

KRAJINA, V. J.
Bioclimatic Zones of British Columbia.
Vancouver: University of British Columbia,
Botanical Series No. 1, 1959.

SABINA, ANN P.
*Rock and Mineral Collecting in Canada,
Vol. 1.*
Ottawa: Geological Survey of Canada,
Misc. Report No. 8, 1966.

PLANTS

BANDONI, R. J. and SZCZAWINSKI, A. F.
*Guide to Common Mushrooms of British
Columbia.*
Victoria: Provincial Museum, Handbook
Series No. 24.

CUNNINGHAM, G. C.
Forest Flora of Canada.
Ottawa: Queen's Printer, Bulletin 121,
Department of Forestry and Rural
Development.

DAVIS, R. J.
Flora of Idaho.
Dubuque, Iowa: W. C. Brown Co., 1952.

EASTHAM, J. W.
*Supplement to Flora of Southern British
Columbia and Vancouver Island.*
Victoria: Provincial Museum, Special
Publication No. 1, 1947.

GARMAN, E. H.
*Pocket Guide to Trees and Shrubs in
British Columbia.*
Victoria: B.C. Forest Service, 1963.

GUBERLET, MURIEL L.
Seaweeds at Ebb Tide.
Seattle: University of Washington Press,
1956.

HARDY, G. A. and HARDY, W. J.
Wild Flowers in the Pacific Northwest.
Saskatoon: H. R. Larson Pub. Co., 1964.

HENRY, J. K.
Flora of Southern British Columbia and Vancouver Island.
Toronto: W. J. Gage and Co., 1915.

HITCHCOCK, C. L., CRONQUIST, A.,
OWNBEY, M. and THOMPSON, J. W.
Vascular Plants of the Pacific Northwest
(in 5 vols.)
Seattle: University of Washington Press,
1955-1964.

HUBBARD, W. A.
Grasses of British Columbia.
Victoria: Provincial Museum, Handbook
Series No. 9, 1955.

KIRK, RUTH.
Olympic Rain Forest.
Seattle: University of Washington Press,
1966.

KRAJINA, V. J. (editor).
Ecology of Western North America.
Vancouver: University of British Columbia,
1965.

KRAJINA, V. J. (editor).
Ecology of the Forests of the Pacific Northwest.
Vancouver: University of British Columbia,
Department of Botany annual research
reports, commencing 1962.

LYONS, C. P.
Trees, Shrubs and Flowers to Know in British Columbia.
Vancouver: Dent and Sons, 1965.

Native Trees of Canada.
Ottawa: Queen's Printer, Bulletin 61,
Department of Forestry and Rural
Development, 1956.

PECK, M. E.
Manual of the Higher Plants of Oregon.
Portland, Oregon: Binfords and Mort, 1941.

ROWE, J. S.
Forest Regions of Canada.
Ottawa: Queen's Printer, Bulletin 123,
Department of Northern Affairs and
National Resources, 1966.

SCAGEL, ROBERT F.
Guide to Common Seaweeds of British Columbia.
Victoria: Provincial Museum, Handbook
Series No. 27, 1967.

SCAGEL, ROBERT F.
Marine Plant Resources of British Columbia.
Ottawa: Fisheries Research Board of
Canada, Bulletin No. 127, 1961.

SZCZAWINSKI, ADAM F.
The Heather Family of British Columbia.
Victoria: Provincial Museum, Handbook
Series No. 19, 1962.

SZCZAWINSKI, ADAM F.
The Orchids of British Columbia.
Victoria: Provincial Museum, Handbook
Series No. 16, 1959.

SZCZAWINSKI, ADAM F. and HARDY, GEORGE A.
Guide to Common Edible Plants of British Columbia.
Victoria: Provincial Museum, Handbook
Series No. 20, 1967.

TAYLOR, T. M. C.
The Ferns and Fern-allies of British Columbia.
Victoria: Provincial Museum, Handbook
Series No. 12, 1963.

TAYLOR, T. M. C.
The Lily Family of British Columbia.
Victoria: Provincial Museum.

ANIMALS

AMOS, WILLIAM H.
The Life of the Seashore.
Toronto: McGraw-Hill, 1966.

BENDELL, J.F. and ELLIOTT, P.W.
Behaviour and Regulation of Numbers in Blue Grouse.
Ottawa: Canadian Wildlife Service, Report
Series No. 4, 1967.

BRAMHALL, G.
Marine Borers and Wooden Piling in British Columbia Waters.
Ottawa: Queen's Printer, Department of
Forestry, Publication No. 1138, 1966.

BURT, W. H.
A Field Guide to the Mammals.
Boston: Houghton Mifflin, 1964.

CAHALANE, VICTOR H.
Mammals of North America.
New York: Macmillan, 1954.

CARL, G. CLIFFORD.
Amphibians of British Columbia.
Victoria: Provincial Museum, Handbook
Series No. 2, 1966.

CARL, G. CLIFFORD.
Guide to Marine Life of British Columbia.
Victoria: Provincial Museum, Handbook
Series No. 21, 1966.

CARL, G. CLIFFORD.
Reptiles of British Columbia.
Victoria: Provincial Museum, Handbook
Series No. 3, 1960.

CARL, G. CLIFFORD.
Some Common Marine Fishes of British Columbia.
Victoria: Provincial Museum, Handbook
Series No. 23, 1964.

CARL, G. CLIFFORD, CLEMENS, W. A. and
LINDSEY, C. C.
The Fresh-water Fishes of British Columbia.
Victoria: Provincial Museum, Handbook
Series No. 5, 4th ed., 1967.

CARL, G. CLIFFORD and GUIGUET, C. J.
Alien Animals in British Columbia.
Victoria: Provincial Museum, Handbook
Series No. 14, 1958.

CARRINGTON, RICHARD.
A Biography of the Sea.
London: New English Library, Four Square
Edition, 1965.

CLEMENS, W. A. and WILBY, G. V.
Fishes of the Pacific Coast of Canada.
Ottawa: Queen's Printer, Fisheries Research
Board of Canada, Bulletin 68, 1961.

COKER, R. E.
This Great and Wide Sea.
New York: Harper and Brothers, Harper
Torchbook Edition, 1962.

CORNWALL, IRA E.
The Barnacles of British Columbia.
Victoria: Provincial Museum, Handbook
Series No. 7, 1955.

DAVIDSON, A. R.
Annotated List of the Birds of Southern Vancouver Island.
Victoria: Victoria Natural History Society,
1966.

DRENT, R. H. and GUIGUET, C. J.
A Catalogue of British Columbia Sea-bird Colonies.
Victoria: Provincial Museum, Occasional
Papers, No. 12, 1961.

EDWARDS, R. Y.
Birds Seen in Active Pass, B.C.
1965.

FOSTER, J. BRISTOL.
Evolution of the Mammals of the Queen Charlotte Islands, B.C.
Victoria: Provincial Museum, Occasional
Papers, No. 14, 1965.

GODFREY, W. EARL.
The Birds of Canada.
Ottawa: National Museum of Canada, 1966.

GRIFFITH, LELA M.
The Intertidal Univalves of British Columbia.
Victoria: Provincial Museum, Handbook
Series No. 26, 1967.

GUBERLET, MURIEL L.
Animals of the Seashore.
Portland, Oregon: Binfords and Mort, 1949.

GUIGUET, C. J.
The Birds of British Columbia.
Victoria: Provincial Museum, Handbook
Series:
Woodpeckers and Crows, No. 6.
Shorebirds, No. 8, 1955.
Upland Game Birds, No. 10, 1961.
Gulls, Terns, No. 13, 1967.
Waterfowl, No. 15, 1967.
Owls, No. 18, 1960.
Chickadees, Thrushes, etc., No. 22, 1964.

HAIG-BROWN, RODERICK.
Canada's Pacific Salmon.
Ottawa: Department of Fisheries, 1956.

HAIG-BROWN, RODERICK.
Return to the River.
New York: W. Morrow and Co., 1941.

HASLER, ARTHUR D.
*Homing of Salmon—Underwater
Guideposts.*
Madison, Wisconsin: University of
Wisconsin Press, 1966.

JOHNSON, M. E. and SNOOK, H. J.
Seashore Animals of the Pacific Coast.
New York: Dover Publications, reprinted
1967.

MCTAGGART-COWAN, I. and GUIGUET, C. J.
Mammals of British Columbia.
Victoria: Provincial Museum, Handbook
Series No. 11, 1965.

MUNRO, J. A. and MCTAGGART-COWAN, I.
*A Review of the Bird Fauna of British
Columbia.*
Victoria: Provincial Museum, Special
Publication No. 2, 1947.

MYRES, M. T.
The European Starling in British Columbia.
Victoria: Provincial Museum, Occasional
Papers, No. 11, 1958.

NORMAN, J. R. and FRASER, F. C.
*Field Book of Giant Fishes, Whales and
Dolphins.*
Toronto: Thomas Allen, 1949.

OUTRAM, DONALD N.
Canada's Pacific Herring.
Ottawa: Queen's Printer, Department of
Fisheries, 1965.

PETERSON, ROGER TORY.
A Field Guide to Western Birds.
Boston: Houghton Mifflin, 1961.

PIKE, GORDON C.
*Guide to the Whales, Porpoises and Dolphins
of the Northeast Pacific and Arctic Waters
of Canada and Alaska.*
Ottawa: Fisheries Research Board of
Canada, Circular No. 32, 1956.

PIKE, GORDON C. and GIOVANDO, L.
*Whales and Dolphins of the West Coast of
Canada.*
Ottawa: Fisheries Research Board, Circular
No. 68, 1963.

POUGH, RICHARD II.
Audubon Western Bird Guide.
Toronto: Doubleday, 1951.

QUAYLE, D. B.
Edible Molluscs of British Columbia.
Victoria: Department of Fisheries, 1955.

QUAYLE, D. B.
The Intertidal Bivalves of British Columbia.
Victoria: Provincial Museum, Handbook
Series No. 17, 1960.

RICKETTS, EDWARD F. and CALVIN, JACK.
Between Pacific Tides.
Stanford, California: Stanford University
Press, 1962.

ROBBINS, CHANDLER S., BRUUN, BERTEL and
ZIM, HERBERT S.
*Birds of North America—a Guide to Field
Identification.*
New York: Golden Press, 1966.

*Salmon of the North Pacific Ocean,
Parts I - IX.*
Vancouver: International North Pacific
Fisheries Commission, 1963-1966.

Salmon—The Living Resource.
Vancouver: Salute the Salmon Committee,
1967.

SMITH, LYNWOOD.
*Common Seashore Animals of the Pacific
Northwest.*
Healdsburg, California: Naturegraph Ocean
Guidebooks, 1962.

SPALDING, D. J.
*Comparative Feeding Habits of the Fur Seal,
Seal, Sea Lion and Harbour Seal on the
British Columbia Coast.*
Ottawa: Fisheries Research Board of
Canada, Bulletin No. 146, 1964.

VERMEER, KEES.
*The Breeding Ecology of the Glaucous-
winged Gull.*
Victoria: Provincial Museum, Occasional
Papers, No. 13, 1963.

WOODING, F. H.
The Angler's Book of Canadian Fishes.
Don Mills, Ontario: Collins, 1959.

MISCELLANEOUS

Canadian Audubon.
Toronto: Canadian Audubon Society.

Canadian Field-Naturalist.
Ottawa: Ottawa Field-Naturalists' Club.

Condor.
Berkeley, California: Cooper Ornithological
Society, Museum of Vertebrate Zoology.

FARB, PETER.
Face of North America.
New York: Harper and Row, 1963.

HAIG-BROWN, RODERICK.
The Living Land.
Toronto: Macmillan, 1961.

Murrelet.
Seattle: Pacific Northwest Bird and Mammal
Society, Washington State Museum.

Pacific Search.
Seattle: Pacific Search Inc.

SHELFORD, VICTOR E.
The Ecology of North America.
Urbana, Illinois: University of Illinois Press,
1963.

REGIONAL INFORMATION

Large-scale maps and other information on
the Pacific Coast region can be obtained
at moderate cost from: Department of Lands,
Forests, and Water Resources, Victoria,
British Columbia; Department of Recreation
and Conservation, Victoria; Canada
Department of Energy, Mines and Resources,
601 Booth Street, Ottawa, Ontario.
A selection of film strips and slides is available
from: National Film Board, P.O. Box 6100,
Montreal, Quebec.

INDEX

ACKNOWLEDGEMENTS

The author and editors wish to acknowledge with gratitude the co-operation and assistance of the following. For guidance and instruction on field trips with the author: Wayne Campbell, Murray Matheson, David Stirling and J. E. Underhill of the British Columbia Parks Branch Nature Interpretation Office; Elinore and A. R. Davidson, Ralph Fryer and Mrs. Lavender Monckton of the Victoria Natural History Society; William Morris, Canadian Wildlife Service, Vancouver; David Hancock, Island View Wildlife Research Centre. For advice, information and the use of books and papers: Dr. David B. Turner, Deputy Minister, Department of Recreation and Conservation; H. G. McWilliams, Director, Robert Ahrens, Chief of Planning, and Donald Macmurchie, Chief of Management, British Columbia Parks Branch; W. T. Ward, editor of *Wildlife Review,* Fish and Wildlife Branch; Donald Blood, biologist, Fish and Wildlife Branch; Ralph Schmidt, British Columbia Forest Service; Miss Enid Lemon, librarian, British Columbia Forest Service; G. Clifford Carl, C. J. Guiguet and Frank Beebe, Provincial Museum; Dr. Ferris Neave, Fisheries Research Board biological station, Nanaimo; Dr. E. M. Hagmeier, Betty Westerborg, David Kerridge, University of Victoria; Dr. Vladimir Krajina, Department of Botany, University of British Columbia; R. D. Harris, Canadian Wildlife Service, Vancouver; R. Y. Edwards, Canadian Wildlife Service, Ottawa; Dr. Murray Newman and Vince Penfold, Vancouver Public Aquarium; Roderick Haig-Brown, Campbell River; Allen Poynter, Victoria; James L. Baillie, Royal Ontario Museum, Toronto; Nicholas Seymour, Department of Fisheries, Tofino, British Columbia.

PICTURE CREDITS

Order of appearance in the text of pictures listed here is left to right, top to bottom.

Cover/Wayne Campbell
1/WC
2-3/British Columbia Government
4-5/WC
8/Fred Bodsworth
10-11/Harold Whyte
19/National Film Board
23/BCG
24/Dave Hancock
27/WC
34/BCG; Murray Matheson; MM;
35/Valerie May
38-39/NFB
40/Jack Bain
47/Patrick Fraser
51/BCG
56/VM; VM; VM;
58/Alma Carmichael
57/VM; WC; VM; VM;
59/DH; BCG; WC; J. E. Underhill
62/PF

67/WC
72/VM; VM; JEU; VM; WC
73/VM
78/Public Archives of Canada
83/BCG
88/WC
89/WC
90/WC; WC; WC; VM; WC; PF; WC
91/AC; AC
92/Alan Hook; AH; AH; AH;
93/WC
94/DH
111/DH
114/DH; DH; DH
115/DH;
117/WC
119/DH
120/DH
121/WC
122/WC; WC; WC; VM
125/DH
128/J. H. Claesson
134/NFB
137/WC; WC
139/NFB; NFB

This book was produced entirely in Canada by:
Mono Lino Typesetting Co. Limited / *Typesetting;* Herzig Somerville Limited / *Film Separation;*
Ashton-Potter Limited / *Printing;* T. H. Best Printing Co. Limited / *Binding.*
Typefaces: Times New Roman and Helvetica. Paper: 65 lb. Georgian Offset Smooth.

PRINTED IN CANADA

B C D E F 73 72 71

B